Ecstasy Romance

"YOU DISAPPOINT ME. SOMEHOW THAT SEEMS TOO—CHEAP, EVEN FOR YOU."

"Cheap?" He threaded amusement through the word. "I offer to give up what might be over a quarter of a million dollars for a chance to go to bed with you, and you call me cheap?"

She turned and faced him, chin high. "You're bluffing."

The silence in the apartment stretched endlessly as Devlin watched her, his mouth turned up at one corner. "Try me."

Carolyn stared at him, thinking how he was one of the few men who had ever stood in her apartment and looked as if he belonged. Could she go to bed with a man she hated in order to save her company? She twisted away and stared out into the darkness. "No bet, Mr. Halliday. I made a vow long ago never to sell myself to any man, either in marriage or out."

"Including Jed Lang?"

Enraged, she whirled around to him. "Jed Lang is my . . ."

"Well, go on." His brown eyes were fixed on hers. "What is Jed Lang to you?"

She met his eyes levelly. "He is not my lover."

A CANDLELIGHT ECSTASY ROMANCE ®

PLAY TO WIN

Shirley Hart

A CANDLELIGHT ECSTASY ROMANCE ®

Published by
Dell Publishing Co., Inc.
1 Dag Hammarskjold Plaza
New York, New York 10017

Dell ® TM 681510, Dell Publishing Co., Inc.
Candlelight Ecstasy Romance®, 1,203,540, is a registered
trademark of Dell Publishing Co., Inc.,
New York, New York.

ISBN: 0-440-16939-9

Printed in the United States of America
First printing—January 1984

To Our Readers:

We have been delighted with your enthusiastic response to Candlelight Ecstasy Romances®, and we thank you for the interest you have shown in this exciting series.

In the upcoming months we will continue to present the distinctive sensuous love stories you have come to expect only from Ecstasy. We look forward to bringing you many more books from your favorite authors and also the very finest work from new authors of contemporary romantic fiction.

As always, we are striving to present the unique, absorbing love stories that you enjoy most—books that are more than ordinary romance.

Your suggestions and comments are always welcome. Please write to us at the address below.

Sincerely,

The Editors
Candlelight Romances
1 Dag Hammarskjold Plaza
New York, New York 10017

CHAPTER ONE

The breeze, laden with the sweet, wet weed and fish scent of the Mississippi, fluttered the white cap sleeve of Carolyn Wakefield's summer dress as she danced slowly around the wharf in Tom's arms. On the opposite side of the river the steep bluffs were dark shadows against the gray sky. The night vacillated between the cool air wafting over her bare arms and the warm air radiating upward from the macadam surface of the wharf.

Or was it nervousness that made her skin feel both hot and cold?

As if he had read her mind, Tom muttered into her ear, "It's a crazy fool scheme and you're even crazier to try it."

She was silent for a moment. Then she pulled away slightly in order to look into his scowling face. They were the same height of five seven, or nearly so, and she'd had to agree to wear low heels tonight in order to wring a promise from him to come with her. Tom hated it when she wore heels in the plant. That extra three inches made her tower over him.

Tom turned her in rhythm to the music, and the white drift of a dress with its unfettered fit and scalloped hem swung out around her slim legs. She tilted her head to look up at the park, which was a good five feet above her eye level. She knew that from up there, where people stood listening, she was very visible against the black surface of wharf and the shimmer of gray-green water. She wanted to be visible. She had spent her entire lunch hour shopping for the dress and rejoiced when she saw it hanging on the rack, almost waiting for her, it seemed. Its stark white-ness, its low, scooped neckline, and its wide circle skirt set off her tall slim form and her boyishly short, wavy black hair. The dress exposed a wide expanse of throat and neck and would attract attention even in darkness. And that was exactly what she want-ed. She had needed the white dress the same way a carp fisher-man needed his net. She was out to snag a very big fish.

"If I'm crazy," she whispered, "you are, too."

He grimaced. "You know darn well I'm as interested in saving my job as you are," he said grimly. "Helen will kill me if we have to move again."

Helen, Tom's wife, had definite ideas about how much time her husband should spend at his job. Carolyn wondered if Hel-en's interference had anything to do with Tom's constant job changing and their enforced mobility. Most employers wouldn't be as understanding as Jed was. But Tom fit his special require-ments to a T. "Did she mind your coming out tonight?" she teased.

He gave her a sardonic look, his light hair lifted slightly by the wind's teasing breath. "You know the answer to that one."

An imp of mischief pushed her to say, "Does she still think you're falling for me?"

He laughed shortly, his eyes straying upward to the top of her head. "She ought to realize I'd need a stepladder for that." He peered at her. "She's envious of you and I don't blame her. You're so damn . . . put-together. Couldn't you take an ugly pill or something? Helen wouldn't be suspicious of me if you weren't so gorgeous."

Carolyn chuckled. She had spent far too many years being unattractive to dislike being told she wasn't, but Tom's com-ments had to be taken with a dose of common sense. "Sorry, Tom. You'll just have to go on ordering yellow roses for Helen every two weeks and taking her out to dinner on weekends."

He gave her an owlish look. "You're costing me a mint and you don't even care."

Carolyn arched away to look directly at him. "With the salary Jed is paying you, you can afford it."

Tom frowned slightly. In retaliation he gripped her tighter, pulled her closer, and took another side-step that didn't seem to have anything to do with the beat of the music. Caught off guard, she nearly stumbled. He clutched at her and brought her against him so tightly that her hips brushed his intimately. She pushed him away, bit down on an impatient word, and then let it out when she realized that he had kept her faced away from the park and toward the band, the five-member jazz group perched on the flat top of a houseboat that was tied to the pier. She lifted one elegant black eyebrow in displeasure. "Turn so I can see the park," she murmured.

Tom hesitated, then heaved a small sigh and obeyed her.

She followed his somewhat erratic dance steps automatically, her mind racing, her eyes searching the faces of the small crowd that had begun to gather on the grassy lawn five feet above. There was a family, the children clinging to the lower rail of the restraining fence. But she was not looking for a family, nor was she interested in the young couple who stood with their arms around each other's waist, a rapt, absorbed look in their eyes as the girl turned her head to look up at the young man and smile as if she shared a secret with him. No, she certainly wasn't looking for them. She was looking for a tall, thin man with a smooth, good-looking face, its patrician nose long and finely drawn, the well-cut mouth below it relaxed in an easy smile, the broad forehead topped by a shock of disheveled, coffee-brown hair.

He wasn't there. Or at least he wasn't standing next to the rail or in any of the clustered groups of twos and threes beyond. *But he'll come,* she told herself fiercely, trying to curb her impatience. It was only a matter of time. He was a jazz aficionado and this was authentic jazz, played by a semiprofessional group in a week-long celebration of the river's heritage.

The whole thing couldn't have been better if she had planned

11

it. The hotel clerk assured her that Mr. Halliday would be checking in sometime after six but before eight because the reservation had been secured by credit card, but Mr. Halliday had requested room service for the evening meal. It had been a simple matter to suggest to Art Foreman, the chairman of the Family Days celebration, that brochures advertising the week-long activities be placed in each of the motel rooms on a regular basis. It had been even simpler to hand a ten-dollar tip to a motel maid and be assured that a brochure would rest on the desk of room number thirty-six, the executive suite, by three o'clock this afternoon. Whether Devlin Halliday would take the bait was another matter. He was a private man, who lived a private life.

But his private life is impinging on mine. Her cool, feminine mouth firmed, and her eyes, a deep shade of blue, burned restlessly over Tom's shoulder to sweep around the park that was rapidly falling into shadow, even though all the overhead vapor lights burned. It was nearly ten o'clock. Suppose he didn't come? Suppose she had to seek him out?

With exasperated impatience she realized Tom was dancing her closer to the levee and her view of the park was gradually diminishing. "Move out closer to the edge of the wharf."

"And fall in the river?" A tinge of sarcasm colored his voice.

"I want to see more of the park," she retorted, her nervous state making her words sharp. Tom complied once again, dancing her over closer to the edge. She strained to see in the darkness, peering over his shoulder at the people above them. The wharf was at the surface of the river, the park at a safer height above. The citizens of LaCrosse had learned long ago about the swelling tides of the springtime Mississippi.

The river. If it weren't for the river, she wouldn't be here tonight worrying about "Company Raider" Halliday, she thought, a twist of grim distaste moving her mouth. The company that Jed had thrown at her casually three years ago and told her to make a success of in two or lose was now in more danger than she had ever dreamed in those years she struggled against

12

bankruptcy. And all because she couldn't afford to buy a controlling interest in the stock immediately. She had been overzealous in making sure that her stock was scattered over a wide geographical base, thinking that would keep her safe from a takeover. How wrong she had been!

Damn Halliday and his nine point nine percent of stock. That stock should have been hers. She'd worked to save the company, lain awake nights, sweated blood. She hadn't wanted to ask Jed for the money, she'd wanted to buy stock with her share of income. Now she'd never have the chance—all because Halliday wanted the company . . . her company. The company with one of the largest existing docks on the LaCrosse side of the river.

She had to give the devil his due. He'd done everything in a perfectly legal way, buying his stock from the open market, quietly. She hated him for being so clever . . . and herself for being so blind in not seeing it coming. In a spasm of pain her hands clasped Tom's shoulder.

"What's the matter? Did you see him? Is he here?"

She shook her head. "No."

"Are you sure you'll recognize him if you do?" There was a wry self-mockery in Tom's voice, as if he was aware of the undercurrents of tension in her body that most certainly would have given her away to Jed—and to any other man who held her as closely as Tom was holding her.

She replied blandly, "How much can he have changed in seven years?"

He met her eyes. "How much have you changed in seven years?"

Shocked into silence, she fought for control. It was an idle comment, nothing more. Tom couldn't have known what she looked like seven years ago, but even so . . .

"Well?" he said insistently.

"I'm sure I'll recognize him."

She wished Tom would shut up. She needed to think. She wouldn't have asked him to come, but there was no way she

13

could have appeared at the wharf alone tonight. Halliday wasn't stupid and he would have guessed in an instant why she was there—that is, if he recognized her. So much hinged on that. She doubted if he would, but if he did—she would have to play it another way.

What other way? her mind mocked her. *What other trick have you got up your sleeve? If he remembers your name—*

Why would he? You were one of sixty in his class.

But there was that disastrous interview. . . .

That was seven years ago. He will have forgotten, she told herself firmly.

The girl who had been looking up into her escort's face so adoringly cuddled closer to the shoulder of her young man, and Carolyn was suddenly able to see an area of the park that hadn't been visible before. The tall, lean man shouldn't have been hidden from her view by the embracing couple—but he obviously had been. At exactly the same moment she noticed him, his gaze dropped from the band to her.

With a sudden jarring shock of relief, she thought, *he doesn't remember me!* And in the next instant blood burned in her cheeks. Even in the dim light she could feel that predatory gaze moving over her, examining her face with a cool, clinical precision. Devlin Halliday's eyes were brown, she remembered, a warm, friendly brown. This man's eyes were an undeterminable color of cold, unyielding steel. And his face. Was this really Devlin Halliday? Had she made a mistake? This man was far from the harried grad student who had taught the required course of literature that nobody wanted to take. The man who now stared at her was a finely honed male specimen, his cheeks lean, his jaw hard and firm. Not a hint of compassion or warmth flickered in his eyes. Was this really the man she had thought it would be simple to fool? As if he had read her mind, his mouth lifted in a cynical imitation of a smile. True, she had made him furiously angry seven years ago and she had glimpsed a hint of hardness in that half-hour interview . . . an interview she had never forgotten. But had he? That was the question. Had he forgotten her?

The music stopped. Tom dropped his arms from her and took her hand. "I'm thirsty. Can I get you something to drink?"

The open-air stand was up the stairs to their right, in the park. "Let me," she said impulsively, taking a step away from him.

He caught her arm, stopping her forward movement, and smiled at her puzzled look. "Aren't you forgetting something?" She shook her head. "What?"

"What did you intend to use for money? You didn't bring your purse, remember?"

Her wits seemed to be completely scattered. He shook his head and pressed two bills into her hand. "Don't tell Helen I bought you a drink," he chided her.

She smiled. "Not even just a soft drink?"

He wagged his head back and forth slowly like a doleful spaniel dog. "Helen wouldn't care what it had in it."

She laughed and closed her fingers around the dollar bills. "Whatever you say. Anything to keep peace in the family."

She ran lightly up the steps, glad that they did not come out directly in front of where Devlin Halliday was standing. She reached the top . . . and stood there poised on the cement landing indecisively, her hand clutching the cool railing. As if she were a beacon, Devlin Halliday's head swung toward her. She steeled herself and met his gaze across the top of several heads. Their eyes collided, took measure. Feeling as if she were stepping off a high tower into a headlong dive, she faced Devlin Halliday and boldly began to walk toward him, threaded her way through the crowd, aware of his eyes following her every move.

As she walked the short distance, adrenaline flowed through her veins. Suddenly she felt supercharged with euphoria. The battle was joined. She would met the enemy offensively—take away his option to make the first move.

Should she sound unsure of herself? Perhaps a little. If she hadn't known Devlin Halliday was coming to LaCrosse, she wouldn't have been sure it was he. . . .

"Excuse me. . . ." She was close to him now, the barrier of other people's bodies no longer between them. The full force of that narrowed brown gaze centered on her and swept down the slim lines of her feminine figure that, before, had been hidden from his gaze by Tom's body. At the blaze of some dark emotion in his eyes, her breath caught unexpectedly in her throat, the words coming out on a husky sound. Up close he was even more formidable than he had been from a distance. He was dressed in custom-tailored black trousers and a silky gray shirt open at the throat, but he didn't need expensive clothes to make him stand out from the crowd. His magnetism was immediately apparent to any female within a five-mile radius. The breeze ruffled his expertly cut hair—and lifted the hem of her dress just enough to expose the tanned curve of her knee. His eyes flickered downward and gleamed with a dusky darkness, that for an instant carried a hint of humor. She pressed her skirt down and fought for composure. All her carefully worked-out schemes collapsed. Every nerve screamed at her to turn and run away from Devlin Halliday as fast as her feet would carry her. Instead she heard herself saying in a cool tone, "I beg your pardon. I thought I recognized you . . . that you were someone I knew. I'm afraid I've made a—a really stupid mistake."

"Have you?" He lifted a dark slash of brown eyebrow. "Yes, you must have. I'm sure that if we'd met before I would have remembered you."

She gave him full points for saying the expected thing. But even his voice had changed. It was deeper, more mature. "It happens that way sometimes." She turned to go, aching to escape —when he caught her arm. A flash of sensation poured through her veins.

"I like your style," he said with a cool arrogance, his words fueling the tiny flame that had begun under her skin, "but you need a new line. Men have been using that old chestnut for years."

"And women have pretended to be taken in by it for just as many years," she replied coolly. "You could have been chivalrous enough to do the same."

His voice silky smooth, he said, "Chivalry is dead, haven't you heard?"

She looked pointedly down at her arm and then up into his face. "The news hasn't reached us yet, I suppose."

His mouth quirked. "Where were you headed when you came up the stairs?"

He had been watching her. She opened her mouth to tell him some vague lie but what came out was "I was going to buy a soft drink for myself and my companion." She gestured down at Tom. He stood on the wharf and stared up at her, a belligerent look on his face that somehow reminded her of a pelican.

Devlin Halliday's mouth twisted in a faint smile. "He seems worried. Do you often accost strange men when you're out with him?"

"Unless I'm even more confused than I thought I was, I believe it's your hand that is on my arm, Mr. Halliday," she said icily—and then realized what she had done.

"You do know who I am." He wasn't surprised, she saw, with more than a little alarm. But then perhaps he was used to being recognized. He was, after all, a favorite of the media—when they could catch him.

Throwing caution to the winds, she said crisply, "I was in one of your classes at the University of Iowa."

His face had a closed, unreadable look. "That's been years ago. My classes were large. . . ."

"I realize that. I really didn't expect you to remember me. I was just going to introduce myself and welcome you to LaCrosse and say that I hope you enjoy your stay with us."

"That's very kind of you." He gave her a narrowed, speculative look from under those straight brows. "You still haven't told me your name."

She was sure it wouldn't have made any difference what name she gave him, but some whisper of caution made her say, "Carolyn . . . Smith."

He accepted the pseudonym without the flicker of an eyelash. "It seems strange that I wouldn't have—remembered you. May I buy you that drink in the way of an apology?"

"No apology is necessary." She made a slight movement in an attempt to ease her arm out of his hold. His fingers tightened just enough to make her escape impossible.

"I'm sure it isn't," he said smoothly, turning and guiding her toward the covered stand that had been her original destination, "but since you've already shown me a kindness, I'd be unhappy if you didn't allow me to reciprocate."

He loosened his grip and she felt a distinct sense of relief—until she discovered that he had let go of her arm in order to slip his fingers to the back of her waist and settle them in the curve. He used that subtle guiding pressure only to guide her expertly through the crowd, but she had worn a sheer chemise under her dress and his fingers seemed to burn through linen and chiffon to imprint their outline on her flesh.

She tried to forget his casually possessive touch as they walked forward, but in reality, she felt branded. The accelerated beat of her heart seemed to match the winking lights of red, green, and yellow strung under the eaves of the refreshment stand. She fought for control, focusing on the white-shirted back of the proprietor. At their approach he swung around. Keith Carlson was eighteen and just out of high school. She had known Keith for most of her five years in LaCrosse and had, on occasion, gone skiing with him. He greeted her enthusiastically from his place behind the counter.

"Hi." His eyes settled on her face with their usual adoring look and his smile was brighter than the lights decorating his

18

establishment. "Enjoying the show?" His eyes flickered past her shoulder to Devlin Halliday.

"Yes, very much. I didn't know you were going to be working tonight."

"Got to do something to earn my tow fees." Again looking at Devlin, he said, "You haven't forgotten our date on the first good day of snow, have you? And that day we set up to go fishing—"

She smiled at his enthusiasm, very aware of Devlin's slight movement behind her. "I haven't forgotten." She told Keith what type of drinks she wanted, and he turned away to draw them. After he'd handed the paper cups to her and taken Devlin's money, he said a wistful good-bye. She turned away from the stand and said to Halliday, in what she hoped was a tone of polite dismissal, "Thank you very much. I—"

"I'll help you down the stairs with those." Deftly he lifted one of the cups out of her hand.

"I thought chivalry was dead," she retorted a shade more crisply than she had intended. But her irritation had risen from fear. She was more than a little alarmed at the thought that Halliday was not as easily gotten rid of as he had been to approach.

"I was wrong," he said bluntly, waiting for her to move forward.

She turned her back and concentrated on carrying the cup without spilling it as she walked toward the cement steps. At least when she returned to Tom she would have a buffer against Mr. Devlin Halliday's charm. "Are you always so forthright about your mistakes, Mr. Halliday?"

"I hope so, Miss . . . Smith. Are you?"

The subtle challenge in his tone sent prickles up the back of her neck. How should she answer that? Did he know she was connected with the company? He would, wouldn't he? A clever raider usually had dossiers prepared on the executives of his target. Why hadn't she thought of that? But she was committed to carrying this charade out till the end of the evening. Tomorrow morning at nine A.M. they would sit down at the conference table together, and he would know he had made a mistake. She hoped he was as magnanimous about acknowledging errors in the cold light of day as he was on a warm summer night. She descended the stairs and saw Tom coming toward her, his face almost comic looking as he strove to hide his trepidation behind a jovial smile.

"Mr. Halliday, this is my, ah—friend, Tom Pierce. Tom, Devlin Halliday."

"A pleasure, Mr. Halliday." Tom put out his hand—and Devlin set the paper cup in it. With his other hand Devlin lifted Carolyn's drink away from her and passed it to Tom.

"You won't mind holding these while I dance with Miss Smith, will you?" His voice held a smooth authority that Carolyn didn't recognize from her college days. "It's not often I get a chance to renew an acquaintance with a former student of mine." The nerves in Carolyn's stomach clenched. With one stroke he had rendered Tom harmless.

"Former student?" Tom stood holding the cups, stupefied, his mouth gaping open. *Smith?* his eyes asked. At a warning look from Carolyn he closed his mouth and let the questioning look fade. "No, no, not at all."

I should have seen this coming, she chided herself, as she reached out and tucked the money Tom had given her into his shirt pocket—especially after that blatantly sexual look Halliday had given her earlier. But she hadn't, any more than she had seen the takeover of her company coming. Devlin Halliday had manipulated the events of this evening as smoothly as he did a company takeover.

She turned to Devlin, and the look in his eyes made her breath catch in her throat. A sudden hot wash of anger brought color up into her cheeks. *Damn it all, he's a married man,* she thought suddenly, remembering the fact, the words exploding inside her head. *Why can't he act like one?*

She had been so wrapped up in thinking about his threat to

her company, she had forgotten his marital status completely. Now, when she moved into his arms, her body ignored what her mind remembered. The music was slow and dreamy, but he held her at a circumspect distance—using the pressure of his hand at her waist and wrist to telegraph the direction he wanted her to go.

Why hadn't she worn heels? In her flat shoes she came just to his shoulder. He said, "You dance well."

"So do you." She hadn't liked that space between them, but now, at her soft reply to his compliment, his hand on her waist propelled her subtly closer, and she liked that even less. She straightened her spine and resisted the temptation when what she really wanted to do was give in and let that insistent hand guide her toward the hard male body moving in front of her. This was insanity.

"How is your wife?" she said brightly. "She wasn't able to come with you, I suppose. Do you have children now?"

She felt the tension knife through his body. The hand that was holding hers tightened like a vise. Instinctively she winced.

"I'm sorry," he said, his voice low. "It's just that—I—assumed you knew."

Dread washed over her. "I—"

"My wife died of Hodgkin's disease five years ago."

Her voice low, she said, "I'm very sorry. I—didn't know."

"How could you have?" he countered, his voice cool. "You must have graduated before she became ill."

There wasn't any answer to that.

"And what about you?" he probed, his low voice a husky tone in her ear. "You're not wearing a ring—but in these days a live-in lover isn't unusual. Is there someone waiting at home for you?"

Before she could tell him heatedly that it was none of his business, the blast of an air horn split the night air. A beam of light ran down the river, illuminating everything in its path, turning gray water into a ribbon of silver.

"Here comes the barge, everybody," a man in the band chanted. Another blast from the horn punctuated his words. The night brightened into daytime brilliance, the big searchlight flooding Devlin Halliday's face as he shifted to watch the approach of the ponderous barge, his hand wrapped around Carolyn's waist. Silently, using some mysterious means of unspoken communication, he urged her to the edge of the wharf, and together they watched the six flat carriers move leisurely down the river in front of the towboat. The searchlight swept from one side of the riverbank to the other in front of the floating train constantly, warning pleasure craft to move out of the way, and the air horn repeated the urgent message. This barge was carrying grain downstream, but the sight of it stiffened Carolyn's spine. Devlin Halliday needed a dock—her dock—to transport oil by barge from the Gulf of Mexico inland to the interstate expressway. His particular conglomerate of companies would benefit greatly from the combining of river and road for transportation. The big barges could float oil northward for a fraction of the cost it took to truck it the length of the river. And that was why he was going to buy her company out from under her, because it was easier to buy a company than apply to DNR, the Department of Natural Resources, for permission to build a new dock, especially one of the type Halliday would need with fifteen-foot pilings to support the heavy oil barrels that would be rolling off the barges daily. Instinctively her whole body tensed with anger and frustration. Why her? Why out of the half-dozen companies in La-Crosse that owned a Mississippi river dock had he chosen hers?

"Are you cold?"

She said shortly, "No."

"Something about the barge—bothered you?" he queried softly.

She turned to face him, glad that the barge had diverted him from his clinical examination of her love life. "Are you always so perceptive with women, Mr. Halliday?"

"Not all women. Just the ones I happen to—admire."

The words touched that wounded cord of nerves he had first

22

destroyed years ago, and she said recklessly, "You didn't particularly—admire me when you called me into your office seven
years ago, Mr. Halliday."

In the blaze of the spotlight from the barge, she saw the pupils
of his eyes dilate slightly in surprise. "What in God's name did
I say to you?"

The urge to lash out drained away, to be replaced by the voice
of sanity. "It isn't important."

She turned and was three steps away from him when his hard
hand on her elbow swung her around.

"Tell me."

She ignored the hard tone of command in his voice and shook
her head. "No . . . forget it."

His hand gripped her arm tighter, and he had opened his
mouth to say something when the band broke into loud and
obtrusive song. "Happy birthday to you, Happy birthday to
you." Her head came up in a wildly irrational response. Fear
glittered in her eyes as she waited for them to finish the line and
identify the birthday person. "Happy Birthday, dear Betty,
happy birthday to you."

It was only after she relaxed that she realized how thoroughly
she had given herself away.

His eyes narrowed, he asked, "Is today your birthday?"

"No. Would you let go of my arm, please?"

His hand dropped. "Let me take you home."

She shook her head. "I came with Tom."

"He's wearing a wedding ring," Devlin Halliday said softly,
watching her. "Are married men more your style?"

"More my style than what, Mr. Halliday? You?"

"We seem to be fairly . . . compatible."

She felt the blinding rage sweep over her, but she forced herself
to retain control of the level of her voice. "There couldn't be a
less likely candidate in the world for my affection than you."

She might have thrown the words at a stone wall and gotten
exactly the same response. "Why? Because of some innocuous

23

thing I said seven years ago . . . or because I'm trying to buy out your company?"

"Either reason would be sufficient," she shot back. She hadn't fooled him with her bogus name for an instant, but at the moment she was too angry to care.

"I think we have some things to discuss before tomorrow's meeting," he began in a low, terse voice.

"Caro, would you mind if we went home? Helen—"

It was Tom. He'd gotten rid of the drinks somewhere but he still looked slightly annoyed. A warning shake of her head stopped his words.

Devlin Halliday said coolly from over her shoulder, "Go on home to your wife, Mr. Pierce. I'll see that Miss Wakefield gets home safely."

Tom's alarmed gaze flickered over Carolyn's face. Wearily, she resigned herself to the inevitable. "Yes, Tom, go on home. I'm sure Helen is getting anxious about you."

Tom didn't extend his hand to Devlin this time. He merely nodded curtly to him, sent Carolyn a heated look to chastise her for an evening wasted, and mumbled a sulky good-night in her general direction.

She watched him climb the stairs, taking her last line of defense away with him. She hadn't been able to maintain the fiction that Tom was her lover for a single second. Devlin Halliday was no fool . . . and now she was left to deal with him on her own.

Wordlessly he guided her up the steps and through the crowd. The music of the jazz group faded behind them as they walked away from the blaze of overhead lights into the shadowy darkness of the trees that ringed the horseshoe road inside the park. He took out a key and unlocked the door of a black Ford of standard make and model, but even so it seemed to shrink when he installed her inside and went round the car to climb in under the wheel next to her.

He had parked along the curving path of the park, and she was glad they were leaving before the band finished playing. Otherwise they would have had to wait in line until the cars in front funneled through the one-way drive and returned to State Street. There was no one blocking their way, however, and outside the park she directed him south down Front Street along the river.

"Actually, I live across the river in Minnesota," she told him. "My apartment is up on that bluff."

"Lucky lady," he murmured appreciatively. "You must have a spectacular view of the river."

"I do." She was silent for a moment and then said, "I—would hate to lose it."

"Jed Lang would never allow that to happen, would he?"

Her nails curled into her palms. His research had been more than thorough, it had been brutal. How far back into her past had he burrowed? She took a deep breath. "Jed doesn't—keep me. I pay my own way."

"I'm sure you do," he said silkily.

She gritted her teeth, wanting very badly to do him bodily harm.

"You've learned to control your temper in seven years," he said, going from one outrageous thing to another with lightning speed. "As I remember, you threw a book at me that day."

"You deserved it. You were a pompous ass."

"And you were an obnoxious female who went around looking like a cross between a bum and a woman who ate boxes of chocolate bars daily."

Her eyes glittered with angry temper. "How I looked was none of your business."

"But your grades were. And you were failing my course, Miss Wakefield. On purpose, it seemed to me, as if you were determined not to succeed. I knew damned well there was no excuse for your low grades. Your records indicated you were one of the most intelligent students in my class." He stared into the night. "Funny. I had completely forgotten our little interview, almost as if I'd blanked it out of my mind."

Her temper blazed. "I wasn't so lucky."

25

"Evidently not." He glanced at her. "You did pull your grade up, though, as I remember."

Before she could stop herself, she said hotly, "I also went on a diet and got my hair cut and bought some better-looking pants and blouses because the things you said were so damn cruel."

That did startle him. "Did you really? I wonder why I didn't notice. That must have happened within days of the doctor calling about Judi."

They rode on into the silent night. She said suddenly, "Turn here," and he cursed under his breath and stepped on the brakes. Behind them tires screamed, but no jarring crash came.

"I'm sorry," she said softly. "I was thinking of—your wife."

"So was I," he muttered.

They were both silent on the winding road, but when they arrived at her apartment building and she led him up the inside stairs, she remembered where she had tucked her key for safe-keeping. She turned away, retrieved the warm metal from its hiding place between her breasts, and moved to insert it in the lock.

"Let me." He held out his palm. Confused by a strange rush of emotions, she took the easier course and dropped it into his hand.

He smiled. "It's still warm." He stood fingering the key absently.

"Would you just unlock the door, please?"

He didn't heed her words. He turned the key over slowly, looking at her while he did it, examining her as if her face held a secret he wanted to discover. "It never occurred to me then that your sloppy clothes and careless grooming were a form of defense."

Hot color ran into her cheeks, but her tone was frosty. "I'm no longer your student, Mr. Halliday, and I'm not a specimen in a cage for you to analyze."

To her intense relief he inserted the key in the lock and turned it. Her relief vanished when he followed her inside and closed the

26

door behind them and she realized that it was far more intimate being here with him than it had been standing out in the hall.

"But it was, wasn't it? And I was too young and too stupid to realize how terrified of men you were." His eyes swept around her apartment. He didn't miss a thing, not the salmon-colored pillows on the gray velvet sofa, the creamy white fox fur on the floor in front of the fireplace, or the well-equipped stereo wall to his right. The drapes were open. Though she had flicked the lights on in the apartment the minute they stepped in the door, the view was still spectacular. From this height thirty miles of dark countryside lay below, cut by a wandering dark thread of a river outlined by tiny pinpoints of light from flashing beacons.

For a moment he seemed to be caught up in the view. Then he turned to her . . . and smiled. "But after your performance tonight, I'd say the cure was one hundred percent complete. Or is it?" He tilted his head, that faint smile taunting her. "I suppose there is one way for me to test my theory." He held up the key and his voice poured over her like silk. Her breath caught in her throat. "My mother always taught me to put things back where they came from."

CHAPTER TWO

"It came from that blue bowl sitting on the hall table behind you," she said dryly.

"Did it?" he took a step toward her.

She took a breath. "Mr. Halliday, I don't know what your usual mode of operation is, but I find it difficult to believe you conduct business discussions in this manner."

"What makes you think I came here to talk about business?"

"You distinctly said—"

"I said I wanted to talk to you before the meeting tomorrow morning. I didn't mention what the topic of discussion would be."

She took an angry gasp of breath. "You mean you had no intention of discussing the takeover tonight?"

"You do put words into my mouth in an indiscriminate fashion, Miss Wakefield."

"Perhaps I'm trying to get something concrete out of my encounters with you. Concrete in the business sense, that is," she amended hastily, as a quirk of amusement tilted his lips.

"Were you going to offer me some coffee?"

"Were you going to offer me an alternative to pirating my company?"

He didn't miss a beat. "Well, there is the rather obvious one . . ." He lifted an eyebrow and let the word trail away—and his eyes traveled over her feminine curves. To escape that predatory male look, she whirled away from him and went to stand in front of the floor-to-ceiling window and look out over the river. To the darkness she said, "You disappoint me. Somehow that seems too—cheap, even for you."

"Cheap?" He threaded amusement through the word. "I offer to give up what might be over a quarter of a million dollars in lost profits for a chance to go to bed with you and you call me cheap?"

She turned and faced him, chin high. "You're bluffing." Her voice sounded astonishingly cool. Heated blood pulsed in her ears. "You don't really mean it."

The silence in the apartment stretched endlessly as he watched her, his mouth turned up at one corner. "Try me."

She stared at him, thinking the incongruous thought that he was one of the few men who had ever stood in her apartment and looked as if he belonged. He lounged against the back of her couch and his casual male elegance seemed as much a part of the decor as the tiny replica of the Elmer Howell sculpture of two wild ducks she had purchased for the low table in front of the couch. Could she go to bed with a man she hated to save her company? She twisted away and stared out into the darkness. Old, unpleasant memories surfaced, memories of names children had called her long ago, and the solemn vow she had taken never to have a child of hers know the cruelty of those names. . . .

"No bet, Mr. Halliday."

"Stakes too high?" he countered casually.

"I made a vow long ago never to sell myself to any man, either in marriage or out of it."

"Including Jed Lang?"

Enraged, she whirled around to him. "Jed Lang is my . . ." She blanched and swallowed the word.

"Well, go on." His brown eyes bit into hers. "What is Jed Lang to you?"

Snatching back her poise, she said coolly, "He's my mentor, teacher, friend." She met his eyes levelly. "He is not my lover."

29

He stared at her. "You've learned to say that with a great deal of conviction."

"Because it's true, dammit." Pale with anger, she advanced on him. "What right do you have to come here and make accusations like that about Jed and me?"

"There are any number of people eager to share the story about how he found you working in a record shop in Minneapolis when you were eighteen and brought you home to live with him. There are also a number of other people who are willing to swear he paid the bills for your college education."

"He's sixty-four," she said fiercely, "almost ready to retire. Why can't people let him alone?"

"He's never shunned the light of public attention before—at least, not until he found you. There's just one thing I'm curious about."

"I'm not interested in your curiosity."

"Why doesn't he marry you? Is he afraid you'll bleed his conglomerate dry?"

"Get out," she said, her voice nearly breaking on the words.

His smile mocked her. "I still haven't returned your key to its proper place."

"I'd freeze in hell before I'd let you touch me."

He shrugged. "If that's the way you feel about it, I'll just have to—take your key with me." He made a move as if to pocket the shiny bit of metal.

Infuriated beyond all reason, she said, "Seven years ago you were at least tolerable. Now you're despicable."

His expression hardened. "A lot can happen in seven years."

"Well, you deserve whatever happened to you."

His brows drew down, his mouth thinned. "Maybe I did. But Judi didn't."

She breathed in sharply and groped for the arm of a chair. Her knees had turned to jelly. "Oh, my God. I didn't mean—"

"I'm sure you didn't." His mouth relaxed slightly. "You may feel vindictive toward me, but you don't strike me as the type to

30

let the vindictiveness you feel because of business extend into a more personal type of cruelty. And for whatever it's worth"—he came closer—"if my comments inspired the change from the way I remember you, to the way I see you now—you had the good sense to turn distasteful criticism into positive action." His eyes took a leisurely tour over her. "Right now . . . I don't regret a single word." He moved toward her and his hand reached out. Before she could move away, he dropped the key into her neckline. As the metal warmed from his hand slid to its place inside her bra, she was conscious of the merest brush of his fingers over the sensitive skin bared by the top of her dress. A pleasant tingle warmed her. Still bemused by his lightning change of mood, she stood utterly still and the fingers that had touched her came up to her lips. "You'd better get to bed so you'll be fresh for tomorrow's meeting." His fingertip traced the sensitive upper curve of her mouth. "Sleep well, Carolyn. I'll see you in the morning."

He left her and went out the door, closing it quietly behind him. She might have imagined the whole thing, he might never have been there at all—except that the nerves along her slightly swollen upper lip jangled their wild message of remembered sensual pleasure, and the faint scent of his expensive cologne lingered in her nose. Mentally shaking herself, she crossed briskly to the door, locked it, and fished the key from her bra to drop it into the blue bowl. The metallic clink echoed through the apartment. Still moving with speed and determination, she crossed the room and pulled the drapes, shutting out the night. Inside her bedroom she yanked the white dress off over her head and went in the bathroom to cleanse her face. As she bent over the basin, she felt light-headed. Good God, did Devlin Halliday have such an effect on her she went faint, like some woman in a Victorian romance? She raised her head and saw the pinky patches of color in her cheeks. He couldn't have this much influence on her mental state, he just couldn't. She had to meet him over the conference table tomorrow and she had to be cool and calm—and above all, able to think quickly. She creamed her face and ducked her head to rinse off the grainy cleanser. Again her head reeled and the floor seemed to undulate, as if she were on the deck of a ship.

She grasped the edge of the bathroom counter and wondered what was happening to her. Carefully, holding her head up, she finished taking off makeup and mascara. A few minutes later she came out of the bathroom and walked gingerly to the bed. She felt drained, far too tired to go through the trouble of putting on her nightgown. She fell into bed, the sight of her brown portfolio with its string wrap on the nightstand silently accusing her. She had planned to go over the list of stockholders again tonight. Wearily she reached out for the old-fashioned clock with its double bells and set the jangling monster for four thirty. That would give her enough time to read the list and prepare to meet Devlin Halliday in the morning.

And prepare she would. She lay back, trying to ignore that sensation of light-headedness that would not go away. If only she could think clearly. She had two alternatives. She could call Harve Stanton in Chicago the first thing in the morning and tell him she planned to go ahead with their scheme—or she could try to convince Halliday that the majority of stockholders would not vote to ratify a takeover by his company, a line that was pure fabrication. Several of the stockholders who held large blocks of stock in Leisure Days Houseboats had expressed doubts about her ability to lead the company and would probably welcome Halliday, Incorporated, with open arms. But her methods and ideas had worked, and in just two years under her leadership LDH had begun to show a profit. Would the stockholders take that into consideration? Probably not.

She thought of the letter she had drafted to the stockholders, the letter that catalogued Devlin Halliday's undesirable traits in a legal, faintly clinical way and cast a pall of doubt on his ability to run Leisure Days Houseboats and make a profit. She had felt a pang of guilt about that letter and perhaps that was why it was still sitting in her office, waiting to be mailed out. In a campaign like this, character assassination of the company raider was an old tactic, but it went against her grain. After tonight, however, any second thoughts she might have had about besmirching Devlin Halliday's business reputation flew out the window. He deserved anything she handed out. She thought of the slow way his eyes had moved over her and the outrageous proposition he had made, and under the thin chemise her body burned.

For a moment you were tempted, weren't you? She forced the unpalatable truth from her mind and tossed aside the sheet to lie perspiring in the darkness. She should have left the air-conditioning unit on when she went out tonight. Her mouth was dry, her cheeks still warm. She had to get to sleep somehow. Maybe if she went to the kitchen and got a drink of water . . .

She sat up—and the room swirled around her. Her stomach cramped, and nausea rose in her throat, sharp and stinging. She barely made it to the bathroom in time. A minute later, when the storm was over, she leaned over the basin in blessed relief, one thought racing through her brain. This wasn't nerves. She had a full-blown case of the flu.

She staggered back to bed and lay staring up at the ceiling, knowing it was going to be a very long night.

At room number thirty-six, Devlin Halliday took a key from his pocket. A faint smile playing on his lips, he unlocked the door. From his place beside the round table his assistant, Milt Collins, a man in his early thirties with a head of rusty-colored hair, said, "How was the music?"

"All right." Devlin unbuttoned his shirt and shed it, throwing it in the general direction of the chair that sat beside the bed.

Milt tossed the manila folder he was holding to the table and said, "I thought you were crazy when you first started talking about acquiring Leisure Day Houseboats because of their dock facilities. But are you aware of how their profit picture has turned around in the last two years?"

"I've studied the financial reports," Devlin said shortly, going to his suitcase and pulling out a well-worn gray sweatshirt. He disappeared inside it, tugged it down over his hips. He kicked off his shoes and the expensive trousers followed his shirt. He stood up, pulled on the gray sweat pants, sat down, and put on his sneakers. When he had finished the conversion from well-dressed businessman to runner, he cupped his palms on his knees and stared at Milt. "How long did you say it would take to erect a new dock if we went the route through DNR?"

Milt stared back at him, his green eyes quizzical. "About the same amount of time it takes a woman to have a baby," he said dryly. "Nine months . . . if we're lucky. If we're unlucky"—he shrugged—"it could take longer. And no matter how it goes—it'll take ten years off your life trying to get something done through a government agency." He gave Devlin a narrowed glance. "You can't be seriously considering that. Your stockholders would scream blue bloody murder—and so would your banker."

Devlin pushed himself off the bed. "It was just a passing thought."

Milt studied his boss. "You didn't run into an irate employee of LDH tonight?"

Devlin Halliday's mouth tightened. "You might say that."

"Who was it?"

"None other than Carolyn Wakefield, the president of the company."

Milt's eyes lit up. "Say, I'd like to meet her. She's done a great job of getting this company back on its feet. You'll be keeping her on in her present job, won't you?"

"I hope so."

Milt frowned. "She isn't—being difficult, is she?"

Devlin pushed himself to his feet. "You might call it that." At the door he turned. "I'm driving across the river to jog in Pettibone Park. I should be back in an hour and a half. Let me in, will you? I don't want to have to drag keys and billfold with me."

"Sure," Milt told him, wondering why his boss seemed to be

34

secretly amused about something as Halliday looked at the key he had thrown on the table.

Minutes later Devlin drove across the bridge, climbed out of his car, and began to jog along the trail that ran in curving parallel to the river. The night air was pleasantly warm and from across the way, jazz music drifted, creating a rhythm for the lift and fall of his feet. The park was deserted, only the dark silhouettes of trees rising above the flat island. He ran easily, taking his time, knowing he wanted this running session to last as long as possible. He had a weighty problem to work out and he might come up with a solution if he relaxed and kept his energy focused on the physical task of running.

He lifted his head and glanced around. Pettibone Park was a sandbar come of age. Shadows of picnic tables and round trash containers sat in the center of the oval-shaped island. He ran on, his sneakers slapping against the hard-packed Mississippi mud, his long-limbed stride eating up the distance. God, he felt alive, more alive than he had felt in years. He'd enjoyed his verbal battle with Carolyn Wakefield almost as much as he'd enjoyed looking at her. She had a quick mind and a sharp tongue and yet there was a soft feminine quality about her, a subtle sensuality. Perhaps that was what intrigued him about her, the fact that she was a mixture of conflicting personality traits. Tall and slim as a reed, as graceful in his arms as any woman he had ever held—with a spine like steel. What a will she had. Strange, he still couldn't recall exactly what he'd said to her all those years ago. He had made some rather personal remarks, he remembered, his memory jogged by the things she'd said, but she must have taken them far more seriously than he had meant them. Or had he? Had he felt a pull toward her even then and, feeling subconsciously guilty, lashed out at her? Anything was possible, he supposed.

For whatever reason, she had taken everything he said to heart—and done something about it. She had reacted to him then—and she had reacted to him this evening, he was sure of it. Remembering the way she had looked at him when he touched her, her blue eyes wide with shock, dark and brilliant, stirred his loins. He wanted her. He'd only met her hours ago, and he knew he wanted her more than he'd ever wanted a woman in his life. He wanted to feel that slim body moving beneath him, feel the sleekness of her skin under his hands. He made a sound low in his throat, a sound full of self-mockery. She despised him. And she had good reason to. What was he going to do about her damn company? Everything had already been set in motion, and like a juggernaut, a company takeover, once started, was easier kept rolling than halted. Changing his mind now would cause a lot of people consternation . . . and cost money.

Damn! He must be insane, letting his personal feelings interfere with what had to be done. He quickened his pace, lengthened his stride. The night breeze tugged at his hair, feathered across his hands, making the fine hairs raise just as they had when he touched her. He had only brushed her skin, but its satin smoothness seemed to be indelibly printed on the pads of his fingers. Silently he cursed himself for a fool. He'd known C. Wakefield was a woman, known there would be difficulty. But he'd visualized a woman who would be satisfied with a contract protecting her position in the company until retirement. He hadn't counted on a fiery young woman who had been in one of his classes at the university and had a personal reason to hate him. The name had meant nothing to him at all. He'd had a dossier drawn on her and news photos collected, but he had never associated the slim, dark-haired woman with the girl he had once reproved about her grades and personal appearance. He frowned into the darkness.

The cure had been spectacular. Carolyn was an attractive and successful businesswoman, not some docile female to be bought off with a contract that offered her security. Instinctively he knew she would want autonomy, the ability to make her own decisions just as she had in the past. And he couldn't give her that. He swung around the tip of the island, faced west, and felt

36

the breeze hit him full in the face. He thought about how that same breeze had lifted the hem of her skirt as she walked toward him, and he'd caught a glimpse of rounded knees and slender thighs. A small branch lying across the rutted path cracked under his rubber-soled shoe and startled him. He had taken leave of his senses. He couldn't think about Carolyn, he had to get her out of his mind. The takeover was going to be difficult enough without his being distracted by this damned urge he had to possess her.

Hours later, when the alarm she'd forgotten to turn off jangled at exactly four thirty, Carolyn hit the silencing button. The lift of her head off the pillow was enough to make her sick again, and she staggered out of bed to head for the bathroom. She was reduced to dry heaves now, her stomach contorting itself in violent spasms as it tried to relieve her body of something that was no longer there. The attack subsided, and she went back to bed, her mind reeling, her body crying for rest. She dozed off for what seemed like a second—only to come awake in another spasm that sent her stumbling to the bathroom again. But this time when she returned to her bed, the faint light behind her drapes told her the sun had risen. She looked at the clock. It was nearly six.

She reached for the phone. "Jed?" She scooted toward the head of the bed, under the covers, and brought her knees up to her chin, resting the phone on them.

His baritone rumble came over the wires with a reassuring sound. "What's the matter, Caro?"

"Jed, I've got the flu. I can hardly hold my head up. I won't be able to make that meeting this morning. Will you call Halliday and ask for a postponement? See if he can stay in LaCrosse over the weekend. I should be all right by Monday morning."

"What's the matter? You sick?" Jed always answered his own questions with another question. "I told you you were working too hard trying to head off this merger. I'll send Donna over—"

37

Donna was Jed's sister-in-law, who only just managed to hide her hostility toward Carolyn when Jed was around. If there was anyone she didn't need at her bedside, it was Donna. "No. No! I'm all right. I just need rest. Jed, don't send anyone over. They'll just catch it from me, and believe me—it's not worth it. Please, Jed, I mean it," she said forcefully, knowing his silence meant he wasn't agreeing. "I've got to get some sleep and I can't do that if someone's here with me."

"I suppose you're right. You've got the phone right there by your bed, haven't you?"

Carolyn sighed. "If I didn't, believe me I wouldn't be talking to you. I—" She squeezed her knees up to press them against her stomach, and cradled her head in her hands, not sure which hurt her more. "Oh, and Jed." She hesitated, then the thought of Devlin Halliday's eyes moving insolently over her body forced her to say, "Tell Tom to send those letters out to the stockholders, will you? He'll know the ones I mean. Tell him I want them in the mail today."

Jed agreed to act as her messenger and after several more dire warnings about what he would do to her if she didn't stay in bed for the rest of the weekend and take care of herself, he hung up.

She lay back, her heart beating rapidly, that minor effort of talking to Jed exhausting her. A chill shook her body. She crawled under the covers and huddled there, feeling miserable and alone.

She woke to the sound of another ringing bell. A short explicit word escaped her lips. How could she have been stupid enough to set the alarm again? She groped for the clock, thinking she'd throw the thing into the wall if she didn't silence it soon—when it dawned on her that the insistent buzzing was her doorbell.

Dear God! Jed had sent Donna over after all. If Carolyn didn't open the door to her, Donna would surely go back to Jed and pour a torrent of abuse into his ear.

Carolyn groaned, pressed a hand to her head, plucked her ratty terry robe from the closet, and went to the door. She had

38

it all the way open before she realized it wasn't Donna standing on her threshold. It was Devlin Halliday, looking disgustingly healthy and well groomed in a tan summer suit, and a cream-colored button-down shirt, a brown silk tie that exactly matched his eyes . . . eyes that were taking in every detail of her splotchy face, her disheveled hair, her tatty robe. He said, "My God. You really are ill." He felt strangely, inexplicably guilty. He'd been so sure she'd been lying, using some kind of delaying tactic, and the fact that she'd called Jed instead of him had heightened his suspicions.

"Nice of you to confirm the diagnosis, Dr. Halliday. Now, if you'll excuse me, I'm going back to bed. I plan to die quietly—and alone." She pushed the door forward, fully intending to close it in his face. His arm stopped the door's motion. "You look like hell," he said bluntly. "Have you eaten anything?"

She stared up at him, feeling the familiar stirrings of sickness. In a giant spasm her stomach revolted. She turned and dashed down the hall. She leaned over the sink, and was trying to calm her heaving stomach when he appeared beside her.

"Get out," she whispered, waving him away feebly, but somehow her raspy words and her halfhearted gesture didn't have the force she meant them to have. "Go on, get out." Her voice was too weak to carry any sound of authority. "I—don't want you here—"

He gazed at her for a moment and then bent over and rummaged around in the cabinet under the sink. He came up with a washcloth in his hand, and gently reaching around her, capturing her in the circle of his arms, he ran water over the cloth. "Turn," he ordered her.

"No . . ."

He took hold of her shoulder, and bracing her against his chest as he might have a child, he held her in his arms and began to bathe her face with the cool cloth. She was powerless to do anything but accept his ministrations. The chilly dampness was a soothing balm to her forehead. "Your lips are cracked with fever. You're probably dehydrated. Haven't you even been drinking fluids?"

"Please, I've got to lie down."

He scooped her into his arms and she was surrounded by the faint scent of masculine good grooming and the clean scent that was just . . . Devlin. He carried her into the bedroom. When he laid her down on the bed, his straight brows knit in a frown. "The sheets are damp. Where are your clean ones?"

"Please go. You can't . . ."

"Be quiet. I'll find them."

He strode away, leaving her to lie back helplessly against the damp pillow, conscious to her fingertips of a war raging within her. She didn't want him here. And yet . . . He returned almost at once, her set of yellow sheets in his hands. He stripped off his jacket and tossed it casually onto the overstuffed chair in the corner. Then, with quick, deft movements, he took the sheets off the side of the bed she wasn't lying on, and inserted the clean ones. He rolled her on top of the clean linens, his touch cool and impersonal, and walked round the bed to expertly finish the job.

"Where did you learn—" She stopped, but not soon enough.

Something came and went in his eyes as he looked down at her. "Where are your nightgowns?" he said coolly.

"I—" A blaze in his eyes warned her not to argue. "In the bottom drawer of my dresser."

He returned, her knee-length pink nylon nightie in her hand. "Take off your robe."

Suddenly she remembered what she had on, a see-through chiffon chemise with only strategic bits of lace protecting her modesty. "No."

He made an impatient sound and reached for the belt of her robe. Her fingers closed over his. His eyes blazed down into hers. "My God, do you think the sight of your woman's body is going to drive me wild? Now, stop acting like an idiot and let me get that robe, and whatever other soaked garment you have on, off

40

you. You'll catch pneumonia on top of everything else if you go to bed in wet clothes."

He made her feel ridiculous and immature and stupid, much the same way he had made her feel seven years ago. She gritted her teeth and her hands fell away. With the same impersonal expediency he lifted her out of her robe and chemise, his eyes fastened to hers as he reached for the pink gown. Without hesitating a second, he pulled it over her head, his hands moving down to curve round her hips, expertly lift her, and tug the gown down. She might have been his patient in a hospital for all the attention he paid to her. She felt a sudden, irrational desire to weep.

"I'll get the ice now."

He brought it back in another soft clean cloth. "Hold it to your lips for a bit."

"Why . . . why are you doing this for me?"

"Because I'm the one who happens to be here," he said coolly.

"But after the things I said to you last night . . . and the things you said to me . . ."

"Put the ice back on your lips and don't talk anymore." He took her hand and guided it to her mouth. She did as he asked, but when his fingers loosened, she lifted the makeshift ice pack away and said, "I'll probably give this wretched bug to you. I breathed all over you last night."

Did she imagine it or was there really a smile tugging at the corner of his lips? "Then concentrate on getting well so when I get sick, you can take care of me," he said implacably. "Close your eyes and go to sleep." He went over to the chair and picked up his jacket.

Her lids drooped, then opened. "Devlin?"

"Yes?"

"I—thank you."

His voice came back low and warm. "You're welcome."

She knew he was leaving and she felt an inexplicable sadness.

But there was nothing she could do and she felt so tired. . . .

He went through the refrigerator and kitchen cupboards with a sense of exasperated irritation. Spinach, bean sprouts, raw carrots, tomatoes, brewer's yeast, what in God's name did the woman live on anyway? There were two lemons in the crisper drawer and he could use those to make hot lemonade, but there wasn't a can of chicken noodle soup or a cracker or a slice of bread to be found anywhere. He'd have to go out and buy some. He wanted a decent cup of coffee, too, and he saw with the same irritated amusement that all she drank was herbal tea.

With a sense of acute irony he realized that almost everything she had in her kitchen was either low calorie or a type of health food and knew that he was probably responsible for the eating habits she had developed that bordered on the fanatical. A mental picture of her as she was seven years ago suddenly flashed into his mind. It was the first concrete memory he'd had. In his mind's eye he saw her in shabby khaki pants and a loose-fitting gauzy top of some kind with voluminous sleeves. She had been overweight and had worn her hair in a long, extremely unflattering style. In contrast he thought of the attractive short hair tousled around her head, the slim hips he had clasped in his hands when he'd put her nightgown on her.

Desire stirred, low and deep, and he made a short, derisive sound and plucked the key out of the blue bowl. He went out, locking the door after him. Unless he missed his guess, she would be all right for the twenty minutes or so it took him to find a corner store and pick up the essentials he needed. He'd be back before she knew he was gone.

When she woke again, it was dark in her room. She had slept all day. In the overstuffed chair a shadow moved. She drew in a sharp breath and Devlin Halliday's low voice said, "Are you awake?"

"What—time is it? I thought you had gone."

"I went out to get some groceries." He hesitated and then said with that hint of amusement, "Will I send you flying to the bathroom if I offer you something to eat?"

She shook her head. Her stomach was sore, but no longer in violent upheaval. "I don't think so. In fact, I feel . . . a little hungry."

"Can I help you to the bathroom?"

A faint touch of color bloomed in her cheeks. "I think I can make it by myself."

In the end he did help her to the bathroom. When he saw she wasn't in danger of falling or fainting, he left her there and went out into the kitchen.

"What's that delicious smell?" She came into the kitchen a few moments after he had everything ready. She had showered and belted her slim figure into a soft velour robe in a deep rose color and combed her hair and he thought she must be feeling better to make the effort. There was even a little color in her cheeks. "Coffee," he said. "Would you like some?"

"Yes. What else are you cooking?"

"My specialty. Canned chicken noodle soup. There's also yo-gurt, if you're a died-in-the-wool vegetarian, and hot lemonade. I suggest you start with a dry soda cracker." He guided her to the place he had set for her at the curving snack bar and helped her up on the stool. He handed her a wooden bowl filled with tiny round crackers, the kind meant to be eaten with oyster stew.

She took one and popped it into her mouth. "When did you go shopping?"

"Early this morning. When you first fell asleep." His tie undone, he had rolled the sleeves of his shirt up to his elbows, the fabric white and crisp-looking against his tan forearms. He moved around her kitchen with an efficiency that surprised her. She asked curiously, "Have you been here all day?"

"Yes," he said matter-of-factly, taking the soup off the burner. "Will you try some of the *pièce de résistance*?"

43

"I'm not sure," she said, trying to match his mood. "If I can't pronounce it, I'm not sure I want to eat it."

He set a bowl of steaming hot soup in front of her. "It's easier to eat than pronounce. Here, dig in."

He watched as she spooned a bit to her mouth. "Delicious," she said, and meant it.

"Do you take milk in your coffee?"

"No. This is wonderful. I haven't had home-brewed coffee in ages."

He sat down at the snack bar across from her and because there was no barrier underneath, his knees bumped hers. "Sorry," he told her, and moved away slightly, giving her more room. "You'd think these tall stools would be long enough for my legs, wouldn't you?" He moved restlessly, trying to get comfortable.

"You never could sit still, could you? You used to pace up and down like a maniac when you lectured," she said suddenly, her eyes brightening with laughter. "I thought if I ever had to do anything that made me as nervous as teaching obviously made you, I'd find another profession."

"I wasn't nervous. I was—frustrated most of the time, trying to find a way to break through the boredom. It seemed to come back from those bleacher seats in front of me in waves. I could almost tell when once in a great while something happened, when one of you got as excited as I did about the way an idea was expressed and the beauty and imagination in that expression. I remember once I thought I'd gotten you hooked on Walt Whitman. Maybe that was why I hated it when your grades started dropping."

She glanced down at her soup, not wanting to remember any of that miserable year.

"Had you fallen in love with someone?"

She lifted her chin. "It was a long time ago. I was very young . . . and very gullible."

He studied her, catching her eyes with the force of his gaze. "Were you hurt very badly?"

"You might say that."

"And my frontal attack came shortly after that, I suppose."

"Let's just say that the two things came very close together."

"Why didn't you say something?"

She gave him a steady look. "What could I have said? Please, Mr. Halliday, don't flunk me because I've just discovered the man I love regards me as his entrée to the Lang Corporation?"

His mouth tightened. "I'm sorry."

"I've never told anyone that before," she said slowly, "and I shouldn't have told you. I'm not sure exactly why I did. It must be your insidious chicken soup."

"Truth serum," he said, smiling. Their eyes met. A quiet sort of roaring echoed in her ears. Under the onslaught of that faintly curving mouth and those direct brown eyes, her pulses leaped. *Dear God, I'm not up to this.* She ducked her head and finished her soup and when her bowl was empty, she picked up another small cracker and popped it into her mouth, her mind searching frantically for a more impersonal topic of conversation. "Tell me why you left the university," she asked, in a light tone, "and went into the business of making money."

He didn't answer her, didn't look at her. He slid off the stool, went to the stove, and picked up the coffeepot. "More coffee?"

"Yes, please." The brown head bent over her cup, his eyes watching the pot. She tilted her head to one side, feeling strangely daring. "Are you avoiding my question?"

He turned away from her to set the pot on the stove. "I suppose I am."

"Truth serum didn't work on you, huh," she quipped to his back, half-joking, half-serious. "It only affects females weakened by the flu."

"What business is it of yours?" he said, his eyes narrowed, watching her with a new intensity that made her suddenly very uncomfortable.

"Absolutely none," she said, scrambling back on safe emotional ground, knowing that for several minutes she had forgotten who Devlin Halliday was—and why he was in LaCrosse.

"Why should you care one way or another why I left teaching?"

She was instantly, hotly angry. "Look, I thought we were just exchanging idle conversation. You don't have to make a federal case out of it. I was just curious, that's all."

"And because you told me the story of your life, you expect to hear mine, is that it?"

Her hot temper bubbling, she slid off the stool. "I don't expect you to tell me a damn thing. I didn't ask you to stay around here all day playing nursemaid. I've already gotten far more from you than I ever wanted and I don't want anything more. Now, get out of here."

His eyes took on that steely look she remembered from last night. "Did I say you'd learned to control your temper? I was wrong. You just channel it all through your mouth."

"Get out," she ordered hotly. "Just get out."

"No," he said silkily, "not till I've given you one more thing, something I've been wanting to give you since last night—"

He came around the snack bar in two quick steps and pulled her into his arms. He took her by surprise, and by the time she realized what he was going to do, it was far too late to offer anything other than token resistance. She tried the only other line of defense she had. "No—you'll catch the flu—"

"I don't give a damn what I catch."

His head lowered to hers and the thought blazed through her mind that they were crossing some boundary that could never be recrossed. But she was powerless to move. She watched his face come inexorably closer, the light spill over his male mouth. Had she been looking at that mouth, watching the play of light over the well-cut top lip, the satiny fullness of the lower one, and imagining how it would feel pressed on hers? She must have, for when that mouth that had looked like stone a moment ago settled on hers, its tenderness and warmth shocked her into

46

mindless submission. The subtle molding of his lips to hers made an alien emotion pour through her like water through a flood-gate.

Then he began to move, changing the kiss from sweet posses-sion to full-blown exploration, discovering every line and curve of her lips. He brushed over their jutting fullness and pulsing warmth, nibbled lightly on the contoured height of her upper one just at the place he had touched his finger the night before, and while she was struggling to retain control, he subjected her lower lip to the same teasing capture. His tongue flicked out to pleasure the deep-set corners of her mouth, and his hands moved over her back, their warmth seeping through the heavy velour to her skin. Under the erotic onslaught she made a restless movement and moaned slightly, and he gripped her tighter, anchoring her upper body to his with one hand wedged against her shoulders while the other explored lower and cupped the rounded curve of her bottom to bring her hips more intimately against his, never letting up for an instant the relentless exploration of her lips. Her blood rose in her face and the temperature that had dropped to normal seemed to soar, heating her from within with another kind of fire. She moved as if to break away and he clamped his hand round her head, holding her still, probing under her swol-len, excited lips with his tongue, finding his way first into the tiny space between her bottom lip and her teeth and then into the cavern that waited beyond. His warm pointed flesh played like an imp over her own tongue, stroking, slipping away, teasing, tantalizing until she felt the hot stirring of desire that compelled her to tip her head and allow him easier access to the sweetness he sought.

He lifted his head just enough to whisper against her lips, "Kiss me back, Caro."

She told herself she only wanted revenge, wanted to disturb him as much as he was disturbing her, and that was the reason she intended to obey. But when she raised her hands to capture his face between them and tilt her mouth to fit against his and

47

sent her tongue into the heated hollow of his mouth, her revenge was short lived. Sensual pleasure bombarded her body, radiating from her palms that registered the slight bristle on his cheeks, from her breasts that were pressed against his chest, and her back where his hands wandered over the hollows and curves of her hips and rear with a lazy possession. Her tongue danced over his, teasing and taunting in a delicate feminine parody of his thrusting possession a moment before. He moved as if to break off the kiss, but she wouldn't allow it. She went on relentlessly probing his mouth until he groaned and clamped his fingers around her wrists, wrenching her hands away from his face and thrusting her away from him at the same time. His hands shackling her like handcuffs, he held her a foot away from him, his breathing as ragged as her own.

She twisted her arms, trying to escape his grip. He held her tighter, bringing a cry of frustration to her lips. He let her go at once, thinking he had hurt her. Eyes glittering, she stared at him. "Now what?"

"What do you mean—" he said softly, " 'Now what?' "

"The question seems clear enough to me. Where do we go from here?"

He lifted a straight, brown eyebrow that mocked her. "Into the bedroom?"

She stared at him, her face stony. "That isn't what I meant."

"Wasn't it?"

She wrapped her hands around her middle. "I—want to know what you're going to do."

"Do?"

She trembled, forced herself to continue. "About my company."

His face held not a flicker of emotion. "Am I supposed to feel differently about it than I did a moment ago?" he asked coolly, turning away to pick up his jacket.

"I have a right to know what you're planning," she cried. She closed her mouth abruptly, knowing how desperate she sounded.

48

But if he could make her feel this way after one kiss, how could she possibly go on fighting him across the boardroom table? She tried to force her mind to think logically about what had just happened, but her defenses, mental and physical, already weakened by the flu, seemed unable to cope with the deprivation of his hands and mouth and her mind cried out that she couldn't go on battling with him when all she wanted was to step back into his arms and give herself to him again and again. . . .

"And was that the purpose," he said slowly, putting on his jacket with a slow deliberation, "of all that responsive passion?" His cool words splashed over her like icy water. He said them matter-of-factly as if he already knew the answer. Fully dressed, he gazed at her dispassionately. "Did you think enticing me to your bed would convince me to give up and go away and leave you and your company intact?" His brown eyes were utterly expressionless, his face even more so.

He must think her mercenary beyond belief. And worse, the kiss had evidently meant nothing to him at all. More angry than she had ever been in her life, she shot back, "Last night you seemed eager enough."

His dark head bowed in a sardonic dip. "But you turned me down."

"Did you come here with your chicken soup and your bedside manner and your sexy mouth in hopes I might change my mind?" she cried, driven by some dark, inner storm to have the truth from him.

He favored her with a long, level gaze. "If I did—it didn't work, did it? You saw through me." He gave her a mocking bow. "I'll see you in your office on Monday morning, Miss Wakefield."

CHAPTER THREE

When he stepped inside the motel room, Milt had a message for him. "Miss Lawrence called. She's waiting for you to call her back."

Devlin grimaced, took off his jacket, and threw it on the bed. He undid the knot of his tie, stripped it out from under his collar, his lean fingers unbuttoning his shirt almost before the tie landed on the dresser. Pulling the shirt out of the waist of his pants, he sat down on the bed, reached for the phone, and dialed.

"Room service? I'd like a bottle of Scotch and a bucket of ice and two glasses. This is Halliday in room thirty-six."

When he hung up, Milt murmured, "First things first?" one sandy eyebrow raised.

"You might say that."

"How's Miss Wakefield?"

"She's recovering. Did you get my schedule rearranged?"

"Most of it. We'll be cutting it close Monday morning, but I think we can make it okay."

"Any problems in Seattle?"

"None that Pete can't handle." Curiosity shone from Milt's pale blue eyes, but Devlin ignored it and shrugged out of his shirt.

Bare chested, a scowl on his face, he paced the floor restlessly until the knock sounded on the door. Milt said, "I'll get that," and came back moments later carrying the tray with its dark bottle and two glasses. Devlin lifted the lid of the ice bucket,

50

dropped two cubes in the squatty glass, and poured himself a generous portion of amber liquid. He slumped down in the chair, his thoughts wandering, and raised the glass to his lips.

In the silence the ring of the telephone sounded twice as loud. Milt glanced at Devlin. Halliday seemed unaware of the sound.

On the fourth ring Milt chided, "It's for you, you know."

Glass in hand, Devlin dragged himself up out of the chair, his brows slashing lines of black, and said into the phone curtly, "Hello."

Kristin Lawrence's voice came over the wire, the connection robbing it of its overt sensuality. "Darling, you sound positively furious. Are things going that badly?"

"No," he said, "things are going well."

"I'm glad," she said lightly. Then: "I just called to tell you how much I'm looking forward to seeing you this weekend."

He cursed under his breath. He had completely forgotten that he'd promised to escort the actress to a private party in Beverly Hills on Saturday night. "I'm afraid I'm going to have to cancel out on your gala weekend. Something's come up here. I won't be leaving the Midwest until Monday morning."

There was a shocked little silence. When she spoke again, her voice was cool and crisp. "I was counting on you, Devlin."

"I know. I'm sorry."

"But you will be coming to L.A. sometime during the next month, won't you?"

He cursed himself again for breaking his ironclad rule about divulging the details of his schedule. He hadn't been quite rational the last time he'd been with her. "Right now I can't make any promises."

Another small silence greeted his cool words. "I want to see you—" The husky words throbbed over the wire, and this time there was no mistaking the overt sexuality in her voice.

"I'll call you," he promised, knowing that when he did, it would be to say good-bye.

51

"You do that, Devlin," she said coolly, and hung up before he could say anything more. Perhaps he wouldn't have to call her after all. She probably had any number of men lined up, eager to take his place. . . .

From across the table Milt uncrossed his legs and stood up. In answer to his unspoken question Devlin shook his head. "I won't need you anymore tonight. Go on, get ready for bed. I'll talk to you in the morning."

Under the yellow sheets Carolyn tossed in her sleep, her eyes flickering beneath the pale blue skin of her lids, her sleep disturbed by dreams. *"I'll see you on Monday morning, Miss Wakefield. I'll see that Miss Wakefield gets home safely. You were failing my course, Miss Wakefield. Kiss me back, Caro."*

The husky, disturbed tone seemed to echo in her bedroom. She came awake, her eyes flying open to stare into the empty darkness, her skin prickling with heat, her restless legs churning under the bedcovers.

After Devlin Halliday had left her apartment, she had stumbled back to bed, feeling exhausted, shocked, and sick to the heart, but the blessed oblivion sleep could bring was denied her. She had slept too much that day and been overwrought that night. Over and over again she fell into a light doze . . . only to come violently awake when her mind served up the feel and taste of Devlin Halliday's mouth and the husky sound of his voice. By midnight she had resigned herself to the fact that she wasn't going to get any sleep and threw the covers back. Sitting up cross-legged on the bed, she reached for the scratch pad she always kept handy for late-night inspirations and began to write, rallying her thoughts into some order:

1. Halliday will have court order to obtain stockholders' names. Counter with: Say computerized list has been misplaced. Dig out the old card file, update, and present it to him.

52

2. Telephone Harve Stanton, ask him to call a press con-ference to announce that Leisure Days Houseboats is considering a merger with Amalgamated Shipping. Stanton announcing talks in compliance with SEC insistence for full disclosure to stockholders before a merger takes place. Amalgamated and Halliday Inc. possible conflict of interest. Stanton acting in the best interests of Leisure Days and Amalgamated stockholders.

3. Call together board of directors and change date of annual meeting from April to June.

4.

She leaned back against the headboard and drew long, loopy circles in the blank space. She did not want to use four. It was a drastic action that would shift her own profit sheet sharply from black to red. Her cash flow would be strained—to the possible point of bankruptcy. Number four was a last-ditch effort. But if she had to use it, she would.

After a long endless night, morning came. Grateful for the chance to escape her apartment and do something productive, she went for her morning jogging session and then spent the rest of the day on Sunday in her office, preparing the card file so that it was accurate and up to date. Just comparing it with the computer list took her four hours. Satisfied that it was a genuine substitute for the more accurate printout but knowing the list would be obsolete the moment she handed it to Halliday, she smiled a smile that had little to do with mirth. Her shoulders felt cramped. She leaned back in her leather chair and stretched and felt marginally better. She was as ready to face Devlin Halliday as she ever would be, she supposed.

By Monday morning even her careful preparations and written game-plan didn't help calm her nerves. She jogged for almost an hour in the cool morning and when she returned to her apartment and stood in front of the stove waiting for the water to heat for her herbal tea, she remembered the unselfconscious ease Devlin had displayed in her kitchen and how he seemed as adept at preparing food as he did anything else. Even though he wasn't a gourmet cook, he knew how to open a can and turn on a burner. Of course, she supposed he had done plenty of that when his wife was ill . . . and that was how he'd come by the expertise to change a bed with someone in it, too, she was sure. And learned to have such a gentle touch with a washcloth. The memory of his body gently supporting hers, and the light scrubbing motion of the cool cloth over her heated face, and the smooth easy way he had scooped her into his arms made her skin burn with reaction. Relentlessly her mind served up the brush of his jacket against her arms, the way his eyes had focused on her face, the way his hands had known exactly how tightly to hold her. It was as if her senses had stored the whole scene away on tape so that it could be replayed at will, recapturing every nuance of her sensual awareness of him.

A sound of disgust escaped her throat. She looked at the clock. In exactly one hour she would be facing Devlin Halliday in her office, and she had to forget he was an attractive man. He was a company raider . . . and he was after *her* company.

She managed to be seated at her desk when he arrived at the plant. Her office had three glass walls that looked out over the production floor. She had pushed the long table that held a typewriter, a duplicating machine, and a copier up against the back wall to make room for the round oak antique table with claw feet that she had bought at an auction to use for conferences with Tom and Michele, and Henry, her production supervisor. She had not envisioned sitting down at that table with a raider pirate.

She gripped the arms of her padded executive chair, the one luxury she had allowed herself when the profit sheet began to show its first turn around, and remained seated, watching him walk across the concrete floor toward her, his head turned slightly to watch the crew. Only one houseboat was going through the production line right now, a special order for a Chicago executive, but she had been watchdogging it every step of the way and when the paneling that arrived had not been what she ordered, she'd called the salesman and told him that his mistake was costing her money, and if they expected to continue to do business with Leisure Days, the correct paneling had better be on her doorstep within the week. It was.

Now the wolf was on her doorstep as well. Actually, Tom was holding the door open for him. Next to Tom's slight physique and navy off-the-rack suit, Devlin Halliday looked even more impressive in a light-gray suit and stark white shirt, his silk tie a shade of gunmetal, blue gray. It was an unusual combination, and it set off Devlin's tanned face and lean features to perfection. His hand went to the middle button of his jacket and he loosened it in preparation for sitting down. How could a simple action like unbuttoning his suit jacket unnerve her? She didn't know how, she only knew that it did, sending a kick of reaction through the pit of her abdomen. His eyes lifted to her, and she was glad she had stayed seated and that her old walnut desk was a barrier between them.

His eyes continued to wander over her, and she felt as if he were going over her severely tailored navy-blue suit and white blouse thread by thread. She wore the silky blouse collar turned back over the lapels, and now his eyes played over the bared V at her throat. The way he had brushed his fingers lightly across that exact same place three nights ago bubbled into her mind and with it the thought that here was a man who would know how to touch every inch of a woman's body and give exquisite pleasure while he did it.

Fighting to keep the hot color out of her cheeks, she said, "Good morning, Mr. Halliday."

"Good morning, Miss Wakefield." His brown eyes, clear as crystal, deep as a well, traveled over her face. "I'm glad to see you looking so well."

As if he had said it, she knew he was remembering how he'd

held her, kissed her . . . and the passionate way she had kissed him back.

He's doing it on purpose. He's an old hand at this and he'll throw his sexy charm at you every chance he gets and not give a damn how unethical it is. Keep your head on straight for this one, lady, you're going to need every ounce of brainpower you've got. Don't forget that two can play this game.

He sat down in the chair Tom indicated for him, and the moment he did, she got up, came around her desk, and leaned casually against the corner, propping her long slim legs under her and bracing her hands back against the desk, giving him the full brunt of her slim figure and a smile. "Can I get you a cup of coffee before we begin?"

Not a flicker of an eyelash or a movement of a muscle betrayed a reaction. "Yes, thank you."

She turned and walked to the coffee urn behind her desk, her hips swaying with a feminine grace that was only slightly exaggerated. Directly across from Devlin, she leaned over to fill the white plastic cup. Her back to both the men, she said sweetly, "Tom?"

"I'll fix my own," he answered. "You never put enough milk in."

"Sorry," she said unsympathetically and walked back to Devlin, carrying his cup, suddenly realizing that she hadn't had to ask him what he wanted in his coffee. She had remembered he took it black from the meal they had shared in her apartment. She only hoped Tom didn't pick up on that. The glint in Devlin's eyes told her he certainly had.

Rather than hand him the cup, she set it down on the table in front of him. He nodded his thanks, his mouth in a mocking smile, as if he knew she had purposely avoided touching him.

"We're going to be a little late starting," she said, going behind the desk to sit down in her chair and swivel it toward Devlin. "Jed's running behind and he can't be here for another fifteen minutes or so."

56

"His presence isn't necessary," Devlin said smoothly.

"He has the largest block of shares in LDH," Carolyn retorted, her voice cool, "and he also acts as my financial advisor."

"I should think you would have your lawyer present."

She replied, "Since you indicated you weren't bringing yours, I didn't think it necessary."

Devlin Halliday shrugged, the movement scarcely rippling the excellent cloth of his suit. He leaned back in his chair and looked utterly at ease. "This is a preliminary discussion, nothing more. I wanted to make you aware of the fact that we are interested in buying your company and give you a few of the reasons it would be to your advantage to accept our offer without delay."

She steeled herself, and then let her eyes run leisurely over his lithe masculine figure lounging in the chair in front of her. Though it took all her courage to do it, she started with the dull patina of his expensive shoes and followed a long, slow path up from his ankles in dark socks, past the powerful thighs, over the lean waist belted in a dark, expensive-looking leather belt, to the flat stomach and broad chest—and at last to his face, with its slashing lines beside the well-shaped mouth, his dark, deep-set eyes, his long patrician nose, and his thick coffee-brown hair combed back from his forehead. Letting her voice drop slightly, she said, "What exactly are you offering, Mr. Halliday?"

In another moment Tom would be squirming in his chair, she thought irritably. But once she had started this game, she was committed to seeing it through.

When she met Devlin's eyes, she saw there was nothing there but a bright, mocking amusement. "Cash offers for your stock at twice the market price. A contract that guarantees employment to all present employees for a year. A pledge to do everything in our power to see that Leisure Days Houseboats continues to operate at a profit."

Carolyn gripped the edge of the desk and kept her own smile firmly in place. "Continues to operate at a profit?" She kept her eyes pinned to his face. "Let me ask you this. If Halliday, Incorporated, takes over our dock facilities, what do we use for access to the river?"

He met her gaze. "The dock can be used on a time-shared basis."

"But suppose we run into trouble . . . as we have in the past," she said, accenting those words. "Suppose we need to keep one of our boats tied up at the dock for a week to do repairs. What then?"

"I wasn't aware you had such situations occur."

"I'm sure you weren't," she said silkily. "But one of the reasons our profit-and-loss sheet has turned around recently is because we advertise—and maintain—a reputation for making good on our guarantees. And that sometimes means taking a boat back from a customer and working on it in the water."

"I see." Devlin stared at her thoughtfully for a moment and then took a sip of his coffee. When he set his cup down, he said softly, "There would be no way of planning for such needs, either, of course."

She had gained some ground and pushed forward. "There's something else I should clarify. Ours is a very seasonal business. If a customer buys a boat in April, May, or June, he becomes very angry if that boat breaks down in July." She met his gaze steadily. "His time is limited—his patience even more so."

"You're saying that time-sharing is out."

"Yes."

"Even on a temporary basis?"

"I'm not sure what you mean."

"We would share the existing dock until a new one could be built that met your specifications."

She raised an eyebrow. "And DNR's, of course."

"Of course."

She shook her head and swiveled back and forth in her chair. "No. The easiest course for you, Mr. Halliday, is simply to pack up your marbles and go home."

58

He seemed to consider it and for one wildly improbable moment, she indulged in the fantasy that she had convinced him.

Then he said, "I'll raise my offer of the sweetening package to you and your assistant. In fact, I'll double the original figure . . . the second half to be given in tendered stock."

She fought down her anger at the blatant bribery and said sharply, "I don't want more money."

In a smooth tone he retorted, "But you'll certainly take it if it's offered."

In the sudden silence Tom moved nervously and his chair creaked. She knew he was dying to open his mouth, but she had given him strict orders to listen and say nothing. At the thought of that much money, however, Tom's control failed him. "That's an extremely generous offer, Carolyn."

She leaned back in her chair and gave Devlin Halliday a straight look out of blue eyes that sparkled with temper. "I've been known to refuse better ones," she said meaningfully. Her eyes telegraphed, *like the one you made the other night.*

Devlin Halliday's mouth moved upward in an amused twist. "Perhaps you didn't realize the true worth of what you were offered," he said blandly.

She forced herself to look relaxed and leave her hands draped casually over the arm of her chair. "Oh, I knew exactly what it was worth," she said, her voice faintly mocking.

"What are you talking about?" Tom shot her a perplexed look. "Has there been an alternative offer?"

The building echoed with the sound of a door opening and closing and then Jed turned the corner and walked purposefully across the floor toward them. His timing was excellent, she thought gratefully, and got up from her chair to open the glass door for him. "Hello, Jed."

He leaned forward and kissed her cheek. He smelled of Halston and pipe smoke and she was glad he was there. "Sorry I'm late." His hand gripped her arm, giving her a silent message of assurance while his blue eyes roved her face. At sixty-four Jed was tall, lean, and impeccable in a black pinstripe suit that contrasted with his unruly shock of white hair. He was the kind of man women adored, a man who would exude power and sexual attraction until the day he died. "How are you feeling? You don't look as if you've been sick." Without waiting for a reply from her, he turned to Devlin and held out his hand. "Hello, Halliday. You're looking fit. Still jogging and skiing?"

Devlin smiled at Jed with an easy familiarity that chilled Carolyn. "When I can."

She managed to say, "You two—know each other?"

"We met at a ski resort a few years ago," Jed said in such an offhand way that she wanted to throw something at him. He had never mentioned knowing Devlin Halliday, and she had ranted and raved about the man enough times in Jed's presence to know that the subject should have come up. An angry flush colored her cheeks, while her hands went icy cold. She was overcome with a sense of betrayal. "I see." Her eyes flashed their message of anger to Jed's back as he moved lithely around the table to sit down next to Tom across from Devlin. She took a breath. "Have you two already discussed this proposed merger?"

Devlin's eyes flickered to Jed, who hitched his chair closer to the table and said to Carolyn, "Stop hiding behind that monstrosity of a desk and come and sit here at the table with the rest of us. And bring me a cup of coffee on your way."

Resentment and anger building in her, she stared at him, trying to understand why he was doing this, treating her with such uncharacteristic high-handedness at a time when she most needed to be cool and in control. He looked steadily back at her and something in his eyes made what he'd said the day they'd found out about Halliday's takeover effort come back to her. *If you're going to play with the big boys, honey, play to win. Don't pussyfoot around. Go for the jugular. Find your opponent's weakest point and get him emotionally aroused. An angry man or woman isn't capable of thinking clearly.* Now Jed was using his tactics on her. She bit her lip, swung herself out of the leather chair, and went to the coffee urn. When she turned and walked to the table to place Jed's cup in front of him, she saw that the vacant chair she would have to sit in was far too close to Devlin's extended leg. She waited for him to move. He didn't. Instead he gave her a mocking smile that challenged her to ask him to move.

Fuming, feeling attacked from every side, she moved the chair just enough to avoid touching him and sat down. She gave Jed a straight, steady look. "Two days ago you were against this merger. Have you changed your mind?"

Jed picked up his coffee cup, took a quick sip, made a face at the heat of the liquid, and set it down, his eyes traveling to Devlin, a rueful look on his face. The look didn't fool her at all. She had seen Jed use that face when he wanted to throw his opponent off guard. "She doesn't mince words, does she?"

"No," Devlin drawled, "she doesn't."

"The truth, Jed," she said steadily, thinking that only a moment ago she'd been glad to see him walk through the door and now he was just as much of an enemy as Devlin Halliday.

He leaned back in the chair, his eyes half-closed, his face emotionless. "You've known me long enough by now to know I'm a realist, Carolyn. There's no way you can stop this takeover. You don't have the cash to buy up the stock you need to get a controlling interest—and you don't have the clout with the stockholders that Halliday has. They'll go for him the way a muskrat runs to the river."

Her voice low, she said, "You could have told me this before now."

"I intended to," Jed said easily. "But you got sick. I didn't think my analysis of your situation here"—he made a gesture toward the production line—"would do your health much good." He paused and his face went even more bland. "Devlin told me how ill you were."

Icily calm, she said, "How considerate of him."

Jed turned to Devlin. "Did you offer her the stock tender?"

Devlin nodded. "She refused it."

61

"I told you she would."

"Don't talk about me as if I weren't here." Her voice was low and controlled, but there was a depth of fury in it that brought a slight smile to Jed's lips. "Take his offer, Carolyn. You don't have any choice."

To gain time she raised her head and looked out on the floor. The familiar sounds, the whine of the drill, the blue flash and sizzle of the welder, seemed to sear her soul. Cass was bent over the hull, working on the motor mount. For several long seconds she watched him deftly work with screwdriver and wrench, her mind flying over possibilities. No, for once in her life she wouldn't listen to Jed. There was still her list. . . .

She looked back at Devlin Halliday. The flush was gone, and her tone was cool. "I'd like some time to decide how the news will be given to my employees. They've heard rumors and naturally they are apprehensive."

"How much time?" Devlin's face hadn't changed expression, but somehow she knew he was surprised at her sudden capitulation.

Always ask for more than you want. "Shall we say—two weeks?"

"One would be more acceptable."

She paused, trying to look as if she were unhappy. "All right. I'll take one week, starting tomorrow."

A slight drawing together of his brows told her he wasn't pleased. But he only said, "With no extensions?"

"With no extensions," she assured him.

"I'll agree to that."

"Would you like something in writing? I'll have my secretary draw up the agreement when she comes in. . . ."

Devlin's brown eyes sparkled with amusement. "That won't be necessary." His gaze stayed fastened on her face, and she knew that he was still working over the problem of her easy acceptance of his terms. She said, "Was there anything else you had a question about, Mr. Halliday?" She forced herself to look calm with a touch of dejection . . . and held her breath. Would he think to ask . . .

With an unhurried ease he got to his feet, his mouth tilting at her formal use of his name. "No, I don't think so," he replied.

She released the breath she had held slowly. "If there's nothing further, then—" She stopped, politely inviting them to leave.

Jed rose. "Come over for dinner tonight, Carolyn. You, too, Devlin. My sister-in-law is looking forward to meeting you."

"I won't be able to make it, Jed," she said. "I . . . have other plans."

"Then change them," he told her shortly. "I want you to come to dinner."

Aware of Devlin watching her with a detached, cool face, and one eyebrow at a slanted angle, she said, "I really don't think I can, Jed."

"I'll expect you at seven," he answered implacably. She clenched her teeth, thinking he was at his autocratic worst. If Devlin Halliday thought they were lovers before he saw them together, he would be convinced of it after this little display.

"I'm afraid I can't make it either, Jed," Devlin said in a low, controlled tone, "as much as I would like to. I'm due back into Chicago today and from there I'm scheduled to fly to Los Angeles."

Jed's eyes became slits. "It's Carolyn's birthday," he said.

She glared at him. "That can't possibly make any difference to Mr. Halliday."

"She's thirty today," Jed went on outrageously. "Don't you think she deserves a special party?"

Devlin was smiling in a frank, open show of his amusement now. Her heart sank like a stone thrown into the river. He said, "You're right Jed, she does. I'll try to rearrange my schedule and get back tonight."

"I hope you enjoy yourselves," she said through gritted teeth, "because I won't be there."

Jed frowned and fastened his dark-blue gaze on her. "You'll be there if I have to drag you there myself."

Through this entire bizarre exchange, Tom had fidgeted in his chair, looked out at the plant, tugged at his tie. Now he got to his feet and stepped behind his chair to shove it back in under the table. He shot Carolyn a heated look, a silent message that this meeting had been a waste of his time, mumbled something about going to his office, and walked out the door.

His going signaled an end to the meeting. Devlin unfolded his lean length from the chair, and Jed did the same. Carolyn, finding it intimidating to stare up into Devlin's face so far above her, straightened her spine and got up.

"Did you say seven, Jed?" Devlin's voice was a slow, measured drawl.

"That too early for you?"

"I think eight might be better."

Jed nodded. "Done. Carolyn and I will have a drink while we're waiting. You know the way to my place."

Devlin smiled. "Yes." His dark head swung to Carolyn and his eyes gleamed with amusement. "I'll look forward to wishing you a happy thirtieth birthday."

Her chin came up and her eyes flashed. "Consider it done and save yourself the trouble of rearranging your plans."

He gave her a mocking little dip of his head. "No trouble."

He went then, and when he had walked the length of the floor and disappeared around the corner, she whirled on Jed. "Just tell me one thing. Why?"

He shook his head. "Can't talk to you now, honey. I've got a meeting in exactly"—he pulled back his cuff to look at his watch—"ten minutes."

She swallowed her frustration. "I'll talk to you tonight, then" —her voice was saccharine sweet—"over drinks."

Her control hanging by a thread, she watched Jed stride out of her office. She stood utterly still, watching his tall familiar body move purposefully across the gray floor, every nerve

64

screaming a protest. She loved Jed, but she couldn't take this. It was time to implement item number four.

She pulled open the glass door and went around the small boat-dolly to the cubbyhole that was Tom's temporary domain. "I'll be out the rest of the day. If anything important comes up, call me at Jed's this evening."

Tom lifted his head from the papers on his desk and gave her a noncommittal look. "I thought you wanted to inspect that paneling after it is installed this afternoon."

"I'll have to do that tomorrow. Oh, and call Michele and tell her I won't be needing her this afternoon," she directed him, knowing her secretary would appreciate the advance notice. Michele worked part-time, more or less on demand, but Carolyn tried not to take advantage of the fact that Michele's mother was able to take care of Michele's small son on a moment's notice. Carolyn appreciated having a cheerful, experienced woman to answer the phone, type, and do bookkeeping for her on a part-time basis.

"Don't forget," she said, and walked out the door, leaving Tom sitting there glowering at her. Back in her office she grabbed her purse and raced out of the plant, knowing she didn't have a moment to spare.

Devlin Halliday tucked his long legs and lean frame into the black rental Ford and drove directly to his motel. It was a bright August day, seasonably warm, yet the air held a hint of fall. Whistling a soft, tuneless melody, he parked the car and strode into the lobby. He hadn't imagined it would be so easy. He'd won the battle almost without a struggle. He'd expected fireworks from Carolyn Wakefield and got nothing but a reasonable request for a week's delay in the formal announcement. It had been over almost before it started. He should be feeling good about the whole thing. Why wasn't he?

Inside, the clerk at the desk, a young man with fair good looks that reminded him slightly of the kid who had served soft drinks in the park, looked up—and gave him an odd, considering glance. Now, what the devil was wrong with him? He shrugged the thought aside and went to the elevator.

At the door of his room he brought out his key. Muffled voices came from behind the panel. He frowned. Milt evidently had company. A mild curiosity stirring, he unlocked the door and pushed it open.

A silvery-haired girl lounged on the couch, her well-conditioned body relaxed in a posture that managed to be both feminine and seductive. She wore designer jeans and a lacy camisole top of soft cotton with a wide, square neckline that exposed the creamy flesh of her throat and the mounded top curves of her full breasts. She had kicked off her wedged straw sandals and her small, tanned feet were bare. Kristin Lawrence was only twenty-three, but when she looked up and smiled, there was a wealth of knowledge and experience in her eyes. She was on the fast track to stardom, having first appeared in a hit television series and then moved to films. Her main appeal was a combination of innocence and sexuality that she somehow channeled into a dynamite smile. That smile had done astounding things to him the first night they met. Now all he felt was a mild annoyance.

"Hello, Kris," he said carelessly. "I thought you were working."

The actress's famous green eyes moved slowly over him and he felt as if she were mentally undressing him. She was one of the few women he had ever known who lived up to her sexy publicity. She had a voracious appetite and unbelievable stamina and she was as uninhibited as a tigress.

"That's not a very hospitable greeting for someone who's flown halfway across the country to see you," she said in that husky, trained theatrical voice that somehow managed to convey a feminine vulnerability. Rising from the couch in a fluid movement, she came to him. "I thought since you couldn't see me in L.A., I'd catch you here."

"Aren't you in the middle of shooting?"

"Would you believe the leading man came down with the measles?" She laughed, stepped up to him, and threw her arms around his neck, pressing her hips and thighs against his. "Tony, the producer, is fit to be tied. He's over budget now and that sent him spinning into orbit."

He stood in her embrace, his hands going to the sides of her incredibly tiny waist, the flat of his palms holding her away and subtly creating a distance between them.

She gave him a wicked, teasing smile. "Have I caught you at a bad time?"

Over her shoulder he met Milt's indulgent look. "I'm due in Chicago in two hours."

"Your Learjet can make it in twenty minutes," she said, leaning toward him and pressing her full breasts against his chest. In a lower, intimate tone meant for his ears alone, she said, "Think of all the time that gives us."

He reached up and caught her wrists in a vice grip, bringing them down and disentangling himself from her arms, his eyes moving to Milt.

Milt's fair complexion colored. "I think I'll take a walk."

"Tell the pilot I'll be ready to leave in fifteen minutes."

If Milt was surprised, he didn't show it. "The bags are all packed."

"I'll bring them," Devlin said.

Milt nodded, and let himself out of the room quietly.

Kristin relaxed back away from him, her green eyes glittering, her hands lightly resting on his upper arms, watching him with the concentration of the tigress she reminded him of. "Fifteen minutes doesn't give us much time, but—"

He shook his head. "It gives us no time, honey."

Her hands fell away. "And nothing else, either, I take it."

He shrugged. "Can I offer you some Scotch?"

Her tone dry, she said, "Do I get the bullet to bite, too, while you deliver the good-bye speech?"

He met her steady gaze. "You're a beautiful woman, Kris."

She didn't flinch. "Somehow, coming at this particular moment, I don't think that's a compliment. You really were telling me good-bye on the phone, weren't you?" Her tone was carefully light.

He lifted a dark, mocking eyebrow. "Good-bye? We barely got past hello."

"I think we went past hello last weekend."

He said nothing, merely stood watching her.

She lifted her chin. "You're a cool bastard, you know that?"

"And you're a very sexy lady," he returned in a soft tone.

"Gallant to the end," she murmured. Her eyelids drooped momentarily, then she lifted those artificially lengthened lashes and gave him an open, guileless look that he knew had to be part of her stock-in-trade. "I suppose if I said I'm in love with you—it wouldn't make any difference?"

He glanced away, his eyes averting her scrutiny. "I'm afraid I'd have difficulty believing that."

She turned away. When she spoke again, her voice sounded strange, muffled. "Who is she, some charming blond little Scandinavian who helps her father run a dairy farm?"

Devlin's mouth tilted up at the corners. "There isn't any 'she,' " he said bluntly. "There's only a plane to catch and a meeting to attend and more paperwork and another plane to catch, and more people to see—"

" 'And miles to go before I sleep.' " Her mouth pursed in a mock pout of sympathy. "Poor Dev. You are the typical harried executive, aren't you?" She moved back into his arms and rubbed her hips against his in a slow, provocative circle. "Stay, Devlin, and let's—relax together."

He stood stock still, wondering why her provocative body movements didn't give rise to anything stronger than a mild irritation. He only knew one thing. He wanted to get rid of her. "How are you getting back to L.A.?"

"I don't know," she said, rubbing her hands over his arms, then flattening her palms against his chest. "I hired a private plane to get here, but I didn't make arrangements for the return trip."

"Get your shoes on," he said curtly, taking her arm. "I'll give you a ride to Chicago." It was the easiest, quickest way to get her out of this room—and out of his life.

Against his hips, she went still. "All right," she murmured, reaching up to brush her lips over his cheek, "I'll let you escape my clutches this time." Playfully she bit his ear. Then, in a tone of utter seriousness, she murmured, "But don't think I'm giving up. We were good together. I remember how good—and I think you will, too—when you get tired of playing games with your local milkmaid." She gave him a slow, indolent smile and turned with a languid grace to walk to the couch and thrust her feet into her sandals.

CHAPTER FOUR

The huge oak door of Jed's mansion swung open and the light from the crystal chandelier in the hallway reflected off of Barnard's bald head. The butler's eyes, those narrow dark orbs of some indeterminate color Carolyn had never been able to discern, moved slowly over her, and she wondered if she looked as different as his manner suggested she did. She'd told herself she would need every ounce of confidence both as a woman and as an executive tonight, and she had dressed accordingly. Barnard gathered himself and said, "Good evening, Miss Wakefield. Come in, please," in his normally withdrawn demeanor and made her realize just how far she had shaken him out of it. She'd worn a silk dress in a rich blue color that exactly matched her eyes and exposed several square inches of her throat area above her breasts—and covered her arms from shoulder to wrist with long flowing sleeves gathered in cuffs. The contrast between the shade of her dress and the creamy texture of her skin was startling. The skirt was narrow where her waist was narrow, swirling in a full circle above her ankles. Glittery silver sandals peeked out from under the hem.

Barnard, secure in his shield once more, said, "Mr. Lang will be with you in a few moments," and led Carolyn into the main part of the house to leave her there.

As if she had never been in Jed's house before, she let her eyes move slowly around the drawing room. No other name would have suited the giant cavern with its cathedral ceiling. Jed's heating bills must be enormous. Keyed up, impatient to see Jed and annoyed with him for making her wait, she paced behind the couch that sat squarely in front of the fireplace, smoothing her palm over the rough brown-bark cloth as she walked. Jed liked the rustic look, and he had managed to take the old Victorian mansion that sat on a country road outside of LaCrosse and make it look like a hunting lodge. She had to admit the high ceilings and dark wood cornices kept their identity even though pushed to the limit by the stag's head above the fireplace and the black bear rug in front of it. The battle between elegance and raw primal energy went on in Jed's house constantly, and Carolyn thought it went on inside Jed as well. Perhaps that was what made him so attractive to women—and so successful with them. She stopped walking, and her eyes went involuntarily to the one feminine thing in the room, the portrait of Elizabeth that hung on the wall opposite. The small face of Jed's wife with its heart shape and pointed chin seemed to mock her with a faint smile. When Elizabeth was alive, had her fragile body, confined to a wheelchair, been buffeted by the blantant virility of Jed's house?

She must be losing her mind. She didn't ordinarily go in for this kind of introspection. Restlessly she traversed the length of the room and stood in front of the French doors that looked out over the garden. In the faint dusk the rosebushes and wisteria looked like spiky ghosts. Where was Donna? Waiting for Jed to make his appearance?

A sound at the top of the winding walnut staircase made her lift her head.

It was Jed, magnificent in a black evening dinner-jacket and matching trousers, his black tie impeccably correct. He came down the stairs, tugging at his cuffs, a slight smile playing over his lips. "You're looking particularly lovely this evening, Carolyn."

"So are you," she said with a dry bite that made him chuckle with amusement.

71

"Still angry with me?" He came to her and brushed his lips on her forehead.

"How did you guess?"

"Is that dress new?" She shook her head, not wanting to talk about her dress. He went on blandly, "I wonder why I haven't seen it before. I like the color. The blue matches your eyes."

"Jed, I want an explanation."

He turned away and went to the walnut bar he had had installed to the right of the fireplace. "Just let me get something to cut the dust out of my throat. What can I get you?"

"Nothing," she said crisply. "Jed, stop stalling."

"You handled yourself well today," he said thoughtfully, lifting his glass to peer at the potent amber liquid he had poured into the tumbler. "I have to admit I was proud of you."

"I haven't given up, you know."

He continued to examine his drink as if looking for microscopic impurities. Softly he said, "What are you planning to do?"

She came toward the bar and pulled up the satiny skirt in order to perch herself on the high, padded stool. "Oh, no, you don't. I'm not confiding in you. You blew your cover this morning. I now know whose side you are on."

He frowned. "You should also know me well enough to know that I don't take sides." He lifted the glass to his lips and took a long, deep swallow. When he lowered it, he said, "I'm only interested in one thing."

She supplied the answer. "Profit."

"It's the name of the game, honey." He gave her a narrow-eyed, searching look. "Profit doesn't know who's fighting whom, or whose emotions are involved. Profit is totally without sentiment."

"I have a feeling you're trying to tell me something."

He set the glass down slowly and fastened his dark-blue eyes on her. "What do you think I'm trying to tell you?"

She clasped her hands together on top of the bar and kept her eyes on his face. "That I should have swallowed my pride right

72

from the beginning. That I should have come to you and borrowed the money to buy a controlling interest in my stock two years ago."

His eyes gleamed with pleasure. "You are a bright child, aren't you?"

"A child? Hardly. We're here because I've turned thirty."

"Some of the civilized world doesn't consider a person fully grown until he or she reaches thirty years old."

"Don't try to sidetrack me, Jed." She loosened her fingers and toyed with the ring she wore on her right hand, the sapphire-and-diamond ring Jed had given her last year for her birthday. After a moment's quiet she lifted her head and gazed at him. "Am I being punished?"

His mouth twisted. "Punished? Is that the way you see it?"

"Yes," she said, her chin high, her shoulders straight.

"So you want me to come riding out of the west like Lochinvar, buy up all the stock you need, and hand your company back to you on a platter, is that it?"

Startled, she realized that was exactly what she wanted. "I didn't—"

He shook his head. "I can't do it, Caro. It's too unrealistic. If you're going to survive in the business world, you've got to learn there are no 'quick fixes,' no miracles, no Lochinvars." He kept his eyes on hers. "You made a decision two years ago—based on emotion, for better or worse. Now you'll have to suffer the consequences for that decision. That's the way an executive learns." He lifted the glass and tilted his head back, taking the rest of the drink in several quick swallows.

She watched him, wondering why she couldn't hate him. He had just cut her to ribbons, and she still felt nothing but admiration and a rueful respect for his honesty. No wonder he was successful and wealthy.

Conscious of his eyes on her, she said, "If Halliday takes over the company, I'll be forced to resign."

He brought the glass down on the bar with a forceful crack that made her think it surely must have shattered. It didn't.

"Dammit, girl, haven't you been listening?" He stared at her, his face dark with color. "Are you going to go through your entire life making business decisions on the basis of stiff-necked pride?"

Heatedly she shot back, "There's more than pride involved."

Jed's lips came together in a taunting smile. His eyes glittered. "Now, let me see. What more could there be?" He gave her a pantherish, pure male smile. "Sex, maybe?"

His keen eyes roved over her face, and alarmed that, somehow, some twitch of facial muscle or the expression in her eyes would betray her, she slid off the stool and walked away from him back toward the French doors. "It's not sex." Her voice was emotionless.

"Don't bother trying to lie." Jed's voice sounded muffled from across the room. There was a silence. Then he said, "He's already told me he's interested in you."

She whirled around. "You . . . discussed me with him?"

Jed's mouth lifted in a wide, amused grin. "He wanted to know if he was invading my territory." Jed's smile dissolved into a dark chuckle. It delighted Jed no end to think that Halliday had believed him capable of having a mistress half his age, she could see that. "I told him he wasn't," he went on. "I told him that as far as I knew he had a clear field, that you weren't seeing anyone right at the moment."

Incensed, she stared back at him and just as she opened her mouth to protest the depth of Jed's perfidy, the sound of the doorbell chimed through the house. The butler came noiselessly through the dining room and went into the entryway, and returned with Devlin Halliday in his wake.

The butler disappeared and Devlin moved into the room with a long-limbed stride not hampered by the excellent fit of the chocolate-brown trousers and matching velvet dinner jacket he wore. He thrust a hand through his dark hair, trying with little

74

success to alter its wind-ruffled state with lean fingers. Jed came out from behind the bar to walk toward Devlin, his face creased in smile lines, his hand extended. "Devlin. Welcome, welcome. Did you have a pleasant flight to Chicago?"

Devlin shrugged. "It was uneventful."

"What can I get you to drink? Scotch, bourbon? I fix a mean Rusty Nail, if you're interested."

"I haven't had one in a long time. I'll give it a try." While Jed picked up a bottle and measured the liquor into a shot glass, Devlin turned to her. "Good evening, Miss Wakefield." Behind the carefully polite greeting, mocking amusement lurked. In the long, potent silence he eased himself onto a barstool and gazed at her, his eyes like dark laser beams scanning her from the dark curly tendrils of her hair to the tops of her silver sandals. Then he said, "Will I be accused of blatant male chauvinism if I say you're looking particularly lovely on the evening of your birthday?"

"Male chauvinism is probably the least of your sins," she murmured, thinking perhaps Jed wouldn't hear. But he did, and he lifted his head and grinned wickedly at Devlin as he handed the drink across the bar. "She's a handful, isn't she? Take a real man to tame her."

Devlin held the drink easily, one elbow propped back on the bar, his head turned away from Jed to look at her, his eyes traveling once more over her slim curves outlined in the clinging jersey. "A real man wouldn't want to tame her. A real man would enjoy that streak of wildness."

Jed laughed again, throwing his head back and filling the room with uproarious sound, and Carolyn was glad he was well occupied. Her own color had flared a hectic pink, and her pulse was doing a weird, syncopated beat that had nothing in common with the rhythm of her heart.

When Jed was quieter, Devlin lifted his glass in a toasting gesture toward her and said, "Are you abstaining tonight?"

"Yes," she said, her cheeks still burning with reaction to his frankly sexual remark. Jed's low chuckle echoed through the room again, as if he knew exactly what she was thinking.

Devlin turned to look at Jed, the brown velvet sliding over his lean hips. "Then you and I will have to drink to the lovely lady by ourselves." He turned back to Carolyn and lifted his glass. In the very potent silence he gave her a long, considering look. "To your continued good health and . . . success."

Jed laughed softly. "Her success will mean your failure," he said to Devlin, a gleam of sparkling interest in his eyes.

"Perhaps not," Devlin murmured and lifted his glass to his lips, his enigmatic comment in that warm tone making a sensitive nerve deep in Carolyn's stomach quiver with unexpected vibrance.

The sound of a door closing on the second level of the house drew their eyes upward. Donna Coltrain appeared on the stairway, tall and regal in a gray silk gown with a high, ruffled neckline set off by a serpentine platinum necklace that dangled below her breasts. Matthew, her husband, who was also Jed's business partner, followed her into the hallway, and though he wore a dark evening suit of excellent cut, his own physical presence seemed diminished. Carolyn knew Matthew to be formidable in the boardroom, however, with a cool presence of mind and an intelligence that matched Jed's. He was not a man to be passed off lightly, although his physical bearing was less than impressive. Donna was not above making an entrance and she trailed her well-manicured hand along the banister and walked down the stairs with the bearing of a queen. Donna and Matthew did not live with Jed, but Carolyn knew that Donna loved Jed's house with a passion that bordered on obsession. The Coltrain house, though beautiful, did not have the elegance and structural beauty of Jed's and was located on the other side of the river and several miles into the country, and for that reason the Coltrains brought small overnight bags on occasions such as this, and stayed the evening in one of Jed's many spare bedrooms. The real reason they often stayed over, however, was because Donna adored playing the part of Jed's hostess, and Jed, with a benignly amused patience that seemed out of character to Carolyn, allowed her to do it, to the point of letting Donna give suggestions for party menus to his housekeeper.

Even now Jed watched his sister-in-law and her husband descending the stairs with a peculiar half-smile playing around his lips.

Donna walked to Jed and extended her cheek to be kissed. He performed the expected duty, his face still retaining that look of bland amusement. She turned, her eyes sweeping over Carolyn's slim figure in the midnight-blue dress and dismissing her with a perfunctory nod of the head.

Donna's cavalier treatment was nothing new to Carolyn; she schooled her face to an emotionless mask but not before Devlin's eyes flickered over her in a whiplike glance that told her Jed's sister-in-law's rudeness hadn't escaped him. She felt a small shiver touch her skin. Did nothing escape his sharp eyes and mind?

Jed introduced both the Coltrains to Devlin, who eased himself off the high stool in an instinctive gesture of good manners. To Donna he was coolly polite. Though she tried to hide it, Carolyn could see Donna was more than a little affected by Devlin's dark, masculine good looks and wanted to engage him in conversation immediately, but Devlin turned to Matthew, his eyes gleaming with rather more interest when he clasped the other man's hand. "I had the good fortune to read one of your articles in *Future* magazine. Quite a good piece."

Matthew beamed. "Thank you."

"I agreed with everything you said," Devlin said easily, "and thought you said it better than most."

Matthew, who seldom was at a loss for words, reddened slightly. "Coming from you that's high praise, indeed."

"Would you like some red wine, Donna?" Jed asked.

"Yes, please, Jed." Donna moved with a remarkable grace for a big woman. She slid onto the stool next to Devlin and looked at him expectantly, although Devlin, still in conversation with her husband, had his stool turned outward and leaned against the bar with his back to her.

A fleeting look of impatience crossed Donna's face, and she said huskily, "Mr. Halliday, I know something of your conglomerate. Aren't you currently drilling for oil in the Gulf of Mexico?" Devlin, his shoulder against the bar, his foot hooked casually over the lower rung of the chair, leaned an elbow back to brace himself and swung his head in her direction. Unwilling to watch the woman practice her skilled conversational ploys on him, Carolyn felt her nerves tightened. Devlin's eyes caught hers, and a gleam of something far more potent than polite interest flared there. For a moment she held his gaze, her eyes locked to his. Then she forced herself to look away from those darkly arresting eyes and turned to walk to the French doors, where she stood staring out into the garden as she had earlier, her hands running over the silken material of her dress as she rubbed her upper arms, trying to rid herself of a chill. It was too much, the cool ease with which Donna shut her out, the warm depth of Devlin's eyes as he mocked her. She could cope with hostile salesmen, she could stand up to Devlin in a boardroom fight. But the potent combination of Donna and Devlin together was too much. She heard Donna's well-trained voice addressing another question to Devlin.

Donna was an excellent raconteur and had taken great pains to teach herself about the world of finance. She could keep one of Jed's guests talking for hours and afterward the man would tell Jed that he couldn't remember when he'd met a more charming or well-informed woman. Devlin would soon be as fully drawn under her spell as had been any one of the dozen or so other business associates that Jed had invited to dinner. She gazed out into the darkness, wishing she were anywhere but in Jed's house at this particular moment.

Something feather light touched her elbow, and then, through the silk, a warmth tingled through her bloodstream. Her brain recognized the fact that Devlin stood behind her, touching her arm with just the tips of his fingers, and that his light touch seemed to be burning itself through to the marrow. "This party is for you," he said softly, his breath warm against her ear. "Come back from whatever faraway place you've gone to."

She didn't turn, hardly daring to think what speculation this would cause in the silent little group behind them. But when she looked up into Devlin's eyes, she saw the wicked gleam that lurked there, and she knew he was challenging her, silently defying her to somehow refute his obvious personal interest in her.

There was a discreet cough from the doorway of the dining room, the butler's way of indicating that dinner was ready, and Carolyn thought his timing was absolutely soul-saving.

In the cool dining room, its interior kept comfortable by both a ceiling fan and the air-conditioning, Carolyn allowed Devlin to pull back the heavy, dark English country-style chair with its gold-striped cover and seat her at the table gleaming with an immaculate white cloth and polished silver. Donna sat at the foot, with Jed at the head, Carolyn next to him, and Devlin on her right, next to Carolyn and across from Matthew.

The first course was shrimp cocktail, and though it was one of Carolyn's favorites and Jed's housekeeper's sauce was famous for its piquant spiciness, her appetite seemed far too dull for even that delicacy. A superb chicken *cordon bleu* followed, surrounded by crisp broccoli and tiny glazed carrots, but by the time the desert was brought in, a richly bouffant baked Alaska, Carolyn could barely wait to leave the table. Devlin had parried Donna's adroit questions carefully, talking easily, yet telling her little of his drilling operations, or the administration of his company, even though Donna's careful probing began with the first serving and continued through to the coffee. At one point Devlin had succeeded at getting Matthew to expound further on his views on the recovery of the economy and whether inflation had really been halted or only temporarily stayed, when Jed announced that he would prefer to finish his coffee in the drawing room. Donna concurred, and carefully carrying their cups, they retraced their steps.

It was after they were all settled that Jed, with the air of a child with a secret, left the room. He returned with a small gift, a square box wrapped in exquisite gold flocked paper, a crisp white bow perched on the top like a glorious butterfly. He handed it to Carolyn. She had taken a place on the couch in front of the fireplace and kept her coffee cup cradled in her hands, but now she was forced to put her cup down on the low walnut table in front of her and take the package from Jed. A flush colored her cheeks. She was genuinely surprised. The ring last year had come several days after her birthday, and she really hadn't expected a gift this year.

It was a belt buckle, intricately worked in silver and turquoise, one she had seen and admired in an antique shop. How he had known she wanted it, she couldn't guess.

Her eyes sparkled when she lifted it out of the tissue and raised her eyes to Jed. "Thank you. How did you know I had admired it?"

Jed smiled. "I have my spies."

The slight rustle of Donna's dress was the first indication she had that Donna had moved. The older woman was standing, her eyes on Jed. "Would you mind pouring me another glass of wine?" Her eyes flickered coolly over Carolyn. "That's a lovely thing. It will look good on you . . . with your dark hair and all."

There was a cool malice under the words that went straight to the depth of Carolyn's soul. But she said nothing, though she could feel the coolness in her cheeks and knew that her face must be very pale. Opposite the fireplace the portrait that she had studiously avoiding looking at, the portrait of Jed's wife, who was very fair, her hair the color of wheat, seemed to draw her eyes like a magnet. Her breath caught in her throat and she struggled to keep her emotions from showing. She longed to fly from the room, but that would only make Jed unhappy and he would start an altercation with Donna that would last for days on end. She had heard enough of that the first year she had come to LaCrosse. She had almost gone, not once, but dozens of times. But Jed wouldn't hear of it. He had solved the problem by sending her away to school. Now he didn't bother to look for solutions. He merely looked the other way. As he was doing now. He returned with Donna's drink, handing it to her with the practiced ease of a host. His polite inquiries for offers of more drink or coffee were met with refusals.

Carolyn's fingers trembled as she nestled the ornate buckle back into its bed of tissue. "Jed, I—I hate to seem ungrateful, but I—I have a headache. If you don't mind, I'd like to go home."

"Let me call Barnard. He can bring you some aspirin."

She shook her head. "I really think I just need some rest. I—" She stood up and went to him, holding the little box and pressing her cheek against his. "Thank you for everything."

His arms came up and he gripped her tightly for a moment. "Happy birthday, honey," he whispered in her ear.

Tears burned in the back of her eyes. She pushed herself away, but with her back to the rest of them, she gave him a poignant, glittering look. "Thank you, Jed."

"I'll follow Miss Wakefield home," Devlin said, setting his coffee cup down and levering himself to his feet from where he had been sitting in the opposite corner of the long couch from Carolyn.

She turned to him, a vague sense of alarm chasing away the threat of tears. "There's no need of that. I'm quite capable of driving to my own apartment without an escort." From the bar area Donna watched her, her eyes alive with a predatory gleam.

"But just as a precautionary measure and to relieve my own mind, you'll allow me to follow you home," he said implacably, and after thanking Jed, and saying a succinct farewell to Matthew and Donna, in two lazy strides he had reached her side, taken her elbow, and guided her out the door.

The lights of his car stayed in her rearview mirror as she drove through the quiet night. When she arrived at the top of the bluff and climbed out of her car, the stars seemed to sparkle with an extra brilliance in the dark sky and the river was a slender silver skein that twined over the countryside and reminded her of Donna's necklace. Outside the two-story building Devlin joined her. She didn't bother to protest when he followed her into the stairwell. She knew it would be hopeless, and she simply didn't have the strength.

At her door she took the key out of her purse. When he held out his hand, she put it on his palm. He opened the door, gave her a gentle push inside, and closed it behind her.

Alarmed that he would make himself welcome when she had no intention of asking him in, she said wearily, "I really do have a headache."

"That woman would give anyone a migraine," he replied. "You had some aspirin in your bathroom cabinet, didn't you? I'll get them for you. Go on, sit down on the couch and take your shoes off."

Short of throwing him bodily out, there was little else she could do. Mindlessly she sat and half-sprawled across the couch. He lifted her legs and stretched them out, his hands moving sensuously over her ankles as he slid her shoes away from her feet. She closed her eyes to block out the light . . . and to savor the warmth of his hands on the fine sensitive underside of her arch.

His hands left her, and she heard him walking away. Water ran in the bathroom, his light steps sounded again on the carpeting. "Here." She opened her eyes and found him standing in front of her, holding the glass and two white tablets. When she had swallowed them, he set the tumbler down on the glass-topped table with a little click and eased onto the couch, grasping her feet to bring them into his lap. His warm hands on her ankles sent more shock waves up through the muscles of her legs. "What are you doing?"

82

"Relax," he ordered roughly. "I won't hurt you." He began to massage her feet, finding the tender spot on the sole just under her toes, rubbing it with care and expertise.

It was soothing . . . and disturbing. "Why are you doing that?"

"I'm helping you relax."

The sensuous massage went on, traveling over her heels and ankles, his thumbs probing her flesh with an easy strength and gentleness, his warm fingers cupped over the top of her ankle.

She leaned back against the cushions again, the wine she had had for dinner having a greater effect because she had eaten so little. "I'm not sure I'm relaxing."

"You're not?" The soft chuckle in his voice sounded warm and male. "You're supposed to be."

"Well, what I'm supposed to be doing, and what I'm actually doing, are two different things," she said languidly, watching his tanned hand begin to work its magic on her other nylon-covered foot. "Is this what you do for Miss Lawrence?"

His hand stilled. He looked at her, but her eyes were closed and her mouth was relaxed, and he didn't have a clue to what was going on behind that beautiful face. "What makes you ask?"

"You were on the seven o'clock *People about Town* show," Carolyn said lazily. "From Chicago. We do occasionally get word in from the rest of the world here, you know."

He cursed himself for not having knocked that damn photographer's camera from his hands as he had wanted to. Kristin had restrained him, saying she had been the one to inform her agent of her arrival back in Chicago and that it was hardly fair to turn down a reporter who had come because her agent had informed him of her arrival.

But judging from Carolyn's relaxed posture, it didn't seem to bother her that he had been photographed with another beautiful woman. She had indicated only mild curiosity, nothing else. His mouth tightened. He forced himself to say in a light tone, "Miss Lawrence isn't subject to headaches."

"What is she subject to?" Carolyn said drowsily.

"Publicity fever," Devlin said dryly.

Carolyn chuckled, her long lashes flickering against her cheeks. "Sounds like a virulent strain."

"It is," Devlin drawled. "Incurable, too."

"Kristin Lawrence is a beautiful woman. You have excellent taste."

"I've always thought so," he said in a dry tone. "Nice to know you approve." The urge to disturb her, to make her stop discussing a woman he had known intimately but no longer wanted, made him brush his hand upward to trace the curve of her calf, top the rise of her knee, and discover the first smooth line of her thigh.

Her eyes flew open and she struggled under his hands, trying to sit up and put her feet on the floor. But he had chosen her right leg to caress, and with the leg on the outside in a gentle but unyielding grip, his hand clamped over her knee, she was powerless to move. "Let go of me."

"Why should I do that?" he murmured, leaning over her, watching her.

"Because this"—she gestured at his restraining hand—"you, me . . . is nothing short of ludicrous."

"Why?" he said huskily, leaning still closer, forcing her to lie back against the couch, her eyes fiery with defiance.

"Conflict of interest?" she said wildly, clutching at the first thing that entered her mind, putting her palms up to stop his chest from coming in contact with hers.

"I don't think there's any conflict of interest where you and I are concerned," he murmured, grasping her hands to pull them away and lock them down at her sides, lowering his head to trail his mouth on the sensitive cord of her neck down to the vulnerable hollow of her throat. "I think our interests are remarkably—similar."

"There are any number of reasons why we can't . . . become involved with each other," she said huskily.

"Name one," he murmured against her skin, pushing the

84

dark-blue jersey away and wandering over her collarbone with lips warm enough to set her skin on fire.

"We're business adversaries," she countered in a low tone.

He laughed softly. "No, we're not."

"And we hardly know each other."

"We'll get acquainted," he breathed against her skin, his hand wandering along her nylon-covered thigh, his mouth taking its pleasure over the length of her collarbone, his tongue flicking out to trace the finely sculpted planes.

"Please, Devlin." She twisted under him, her voice throbbing in agony, her body wanting to give in to the wanton invitation of his mouth and hands, her mind screaming that this insanity had to stop. "There are other things, things I can't tell you."

His head lowered, his mouth against the corner of hers, he said softly, "Like the fact that you're Jed's illegitimate daughter?"

Her struggles ceased. She stared up at him in startled surprise, the fast beat of her heart knocking against her chest. He eased away and looked down at her, his face coolly objective.

"How—how did you know?" Her voice was a thready whisper into the apartment. "Did you find out from your research?"

He shook his head slowly. "No, not even my staff are that thorough. Jed told me."

She paled. "He—told you?"

He was watching her through eyes that had suddenly lost their warmth and were cool, speculative. "Yes."

"Why?"

"Let's just say . . . the subject came up."

"How could it?" Her voice was a horrified whisper. "Jed doesn't want anyone to know."

"Does he think he's keeping it from that silver piranha of a sister-in-law? She knows."

"But as long as Jed doesn't openly acknowledge me, she has nothing to go on except her own suspicions."

Devlin said a short, clipped word. "Jed's playing a game with her, just like he is with you. He wants you here with him, but he doesn't want the publicity that would follow his announcement that you are his natural daughter. He's playing both ends against the middle, honey."

"How dare you accuse him of such a thing?"

His eyes narrowed. "All right. Keep your faith in your father if it means so much to you. Just don't think that the way you were conceived or anything that happened to you in the past makes any difference to me."

"I don't give a damn what you think about me."

She had half-risen against him, and now, with very little effort and only a slight nudging of his upper body, he forced her back down against the pillows. "Don't you?" He leaned forward, and his mouth touched her face with a lazy possession, discovering her eyelids, the delicate curl of her lashes, the softness of her cheeks, the tip of her nose. When he moved to her temple, and then down, his tongue making slow and curling forays against the shell of her ear, she moved slightly, her body shivering with sensual tension. He took her mouth then, his lips warm and commanding, their contours fitting expertly to hers, his tongue sliding along the inner part of her upper lip accessible to him in front of the barrier of her teeth, wandering down to favor her bottom lip with the same erotic attention. Torn by conflicting urges, she moaned, and as her mouth opened, the moist tip that had been torturing her slipped into the dark cavern of her mouth and explored every nook and cranny, flicking over the top of her tongue, teasing the point. His hands were working their own magic, one hand pushing her skirt aside to explore the length of her thigh lying so smooth and silky under his palm, the other going under her back to lift and arch her more fully into his embrace.

"Devlin, no," she managed to groan in one last effort to retrieve her sanity; and then, completely betraying herself, her eager hands lifted to clasp his head. She fit her mouth to his and her tongue went on its dark journey to explore the slightly brandy-scented hollow. She kissed him as she never had another man, wooing him with her tongue, brazenly caressing his with sleek little back-and-forth movements.

A low, vibrantly male sound came from his throat, and he broke off the kiss and lifted her, his hands expertly holding her and running down the zipper of her dress at the same time. Under her gown she wore a dark-blue teddy, its lacy cups giving her the slight uplift she needed, and after Devlin pushed her dress down over her shoulders, and pulled her arms from the long sleeves, he nudged a strap of the teddy aside with his lips and fit his mouth to the contour of her creamy shoulder to send more shuddering chills of delight over her skin. Under his warm hand the other dark-blue silky strap dropped, and she was laid back against the cushions, bare to the waist, his eyes taking their pleasure of the rounded mounds of flesh exposed to his searching gaze with their burgundy tips, now hardened with quivering awareness.

"Beautiful is such an inadequate word for you," he muttered, lifting his hand, and gently, as if he were touching something infinitely precious that he would never be allowed to touch again, he cupped her breast. She was still tanned from her time in the sun during warm summer days, and supporting her flesh gently with his long, lean fingers, he traced his lips around the circle where darker flesh faded into paler, his tongue darting out to give her little sensual surprises along the way. When he brought his mouth up to the point above her breast where he had started his erotic journey, he paused, and then moved down slowly to capture her nipple in his mouth and tug at it, gently, erotically. A fierce stab of desire spiraled upward from deep in the pit of her stomach. She writhed under him restlessly, her hips moving in the age-old way of invitation.

In a low, disturbed tone, he said, "Carolyn."

She knew what he was saying. She knew that neither of them could pretend any longer that this was a game, a light teasing encounter. Though Devlin's mouth and hands were controlled, she felt the intensity throbbing through them as if they were her

87

own, and the aching void deep within her clamored for satisfaction. She had never before known what it was to want a man, to want him so desperately that common sense and the fear of having a child vanished. . . .

A child . . . In one last attempt to recollect her senses, she murmured, "Devlin, I—I'm not . . . protected."

He drew back to look at her, and if anything, his dark face looked pleased in some mysterious way. "You're not on the pill?"

She shook her head. She hadn't been, not since that last disastrous encounter in college.

"That's why you're stopping me? You're afraid you'll become pregnant?"

She tugged at her dress, bringing the top up to partially cover her breasts. Desire vanished and in its place, cool logic rushed in. Her skin felt cold, her mind frozen. She looked up at his dark, expressionless face. "There's always that possibility," she said dryly, knowing she had cooled his desire very effectively with her practicality.

"And since you were an illegitimate child, you're not about to risk having one."

His words jolted her. He already understood her far better than any other man ever had except Jed. "You're very astute," she said crisply.

He brushed her hands away and the makeshift cover of her dress with them. She made a sound of protest, and he shook his head. "One of first things you're going to have to learn is to trust me." Lowering his mouth to her again, he brushed a light butterfly kiss on each of the aroused, rosy tips, and when her head was reeling with such pleasure that she no longer worried about the risk she'd be taking, he lifted his head and began to cover her, gently sliding first the straps of the teddy into place and then the sleeves of her dress. Dazed by his tender concern and his apparent lack of ire at being refused, she obeyed his unspoken request to rise and felt his hands at her back, running the zipper up.

"There," he said softly. "Propriety restored. Although you still look sexy as hell." He leaned forward and kissed the end of her nose. "I'll be jogging in Pettibone Park around five tomorrow morning. Will you join me?"

Still dazed, her heart racing like a rabbit's, her mind not functioning, she only knew she had to see him again. "Yes."

"Good." He brushed back a tendril of hair that clung to her temple. "I'll see you then." He rose and stood staring at her for a long moment. She swung her legs down and he extended his hand to her and helped her rise from the couch. When she was on her feet, he turned her and walked her to the door. In the shadowed entryway she leaned toward him, her mouth aching to feel the warmth of his. He gave a small, half-mocking smile and stopped her forward motion with hard hands on her shoulders. "No, honey. No good-night kiss, not tonight. I couldn't hold you in my arms and let you go a second time." He turned and went out of the door, leaving her staring after him, her eyes wide with surprise—and desire.

CHAPTER FIVE

She skirted a puddle of river splash in the road and ran on, conscious that Devlin was shortening the length of his stride to accommodate her. She had never run with a man, and she found it exhilarating to be pounding along at a fast pace with him in the pale yellow light of the early morning. The air was cool, but not chilly, just right for running. There was a short, sweet chirp of a bird somewhere in the depth of the trees, and beside them the river sang its eternal song.

"Did you sleep well?" he asked, the words not disturbing the evenness of his breathing.

"Did you?" she shot back, unwilling to tell him an outright lie, and even more unwilling to admit that his lovemaking had kept her body warm with desire, her legs kicking restlessly under the covers, her skin burning against the yellow sheets until at last she had gotten up and made herself a cup of tea.

He smiled and turned his head to look at her. If he had had a restless night, he certainly didn't show it. Clothed in gray sweat pants and matching shirt, he looked disgustingly alert, completely fit and at ease. If anything, he had probably had eight hours of sound sleep, she thought ruefully, her brow wrinkling in displeasure.

"What unkind thought about me just passed through that agile brain of yours?" he asked.

She gave him a sardonic look, wishing he were not quite so

intelligent, not quite so perceptive. "I was just thinking that you probably slept well enough for both of us."

He threw back his head and laughed, a warm, throaty sound tossed on the early-morning wind. "If you think that, you don't know the male anatomy very well. I came here last night and ran for a half hour just to get myself calmed down."

It was her turn to smile. "Whatever happened to cold showers?"

He grinned. "They're highly overrated. Physical exhaustion and a good shot of Scotch work best for me."

He sounded so offhandedly accustomed to such therapy that something sharp stabbed in the region of her stomach. Her amusement drained away. "I'm sure you don't have to resort to such measures often."

Her frosty tone made him glance sideways. "Jealous?"

"I don't even know you."

"That line is beginning to bore me," he said easily, a faint trace of irritation in his voice. "You sat in class and looked at me for two semesters."

"That was light-years ago. You weren't a company raider then."

Determined to press her advantage, she caught his arm and brought him to a halt. "Devlin."

He turned to her, his face guarded, his eyes shielded by dark lashes. "Yes, Carolyn?" His voice was as cool as her own.

"What happened last night . . . doesn't change anything. I still intend to stop you from taking over my company."

"I never thought it would be any other way."

Suddenly aware of the hard muscles under her fingers and the essence of the man she held and how she was beginning to admire him more and more, she dropped her hand. She remembered the letter she had sent out, the careful wording. "Though Mr. Halliday is the head of a large conglomerate, he is both unfamiliar with the markets and the area of the Midwest and inexperienced in dealing with a small company like Leisure Days, which does most of its business with a limited number of elite clients. . . ." She felt like a traitor, a Judas.

He stood looking at her for another moment and then he turned and jogged away. She bent her head and ran to catch up with him. The instant she was beside him, he adjusted his pace to keep tempo with hers.

"So," he said in an even tone, almost to himself, as if the confrontation of a moment ago had never happened, "now that you've sent out the letter denigrating my talents to your stockholders, what tactic will you use next?"

She twisted her head to give him a sharp look. "You read the letter?"

He grabbed her elbow and guided her carefully around a fallen limb with pronged bare branches that lay in their path. When they were safely by, he released her at once. Her body, with a leap of nerves, protested the breaking of contact with his.

He said dryly, "I'm one of your stockholders, remember?"

Shaken, she fought to keep her voice coolly detached. "You can't expect me to confide in you about what I plan to do."

"Generally the next move would be to contact a firm similar to mine and announce a merger. Have you set the machinery in motion for that yet?"

To her amazement she heard herself saying, "Yes."

"Don't do it," he said flatly.

"Why not? You admitted it was the next logical step."

He grabbed her arm, bringing her to a halt and pulling her close to him. "You can't win, Carolyn. There's no way."

"What have I got to lose?" Her eyes flashed sparks of temper, her hair blew around her head in a torrent of silky black curls.

He stared at her for a long moment. His voice low, he said, "If you agree not to announce a bogus merger with another company, I'll extend my guarantee of employment from one year to three."

She drew in a sharp breath. He had hit her at her most vulnerable point, her concern and responsibility for her employees. "That's outright blackmail."

He said tightly, "I want your company, Carolyn. And I want it now, not a year from now after the Securities and Exchange Commission has finally finished investigating your claim and found it to be false."

Under his calm scrutiny and his slicing words, she seethed. "Why should you get exactly what you want when you want it?"

For a moment his jaw tightened, and the small muscle in his cheek moved. Then the pressure on her arm relaxed slightly and the corners of his mouth twisted upward in rueful smile. "I don't always get what I want"—his eyes flickered over her curves clad in the loose cotton shirt—"when I want it."

Warmed from running, her skin flamed with color. "And if I agree?"

"To which proposition?" His eyes moved over her lazily.

She said heatedly, "To make no announcements of pending mergers."

"I'll have my lawyer draw up the papers on guaranteed employment at once."

Her eyes locked to his, she said, "Have them on my desk in twenty-four hours."

He nodded.

"Is there anything else you wanted to accomplish this morning?"

A gleam flickered in his eyes. "Well, now that you mention it, there was one other detail." His eyes played over her, his warm gaze sparkling with sexual interest.

"Such as?"

"Have dinner with me tonight." It was all there, the masculine challenge, the sardonic expectancy that she would refuse, the mocking male assurance that she would be far too angry to spend an evening with him.

"I'd like that," she said coolly. "What time?"

It was almost worth it to see the faint surprise, the lift of his dark-brown eyebrow. "Eight o'clock?"

Carolyn stood in front of her apartment window gazing out at the view, seeing the rolling earth shaded from tones of brown to green, its landscape dotted with trees, the river a silver twist that vanished toward the horizon. Above it the sky was gray, storm clouds gathering in the west.

She turned away, the soft swish of her lustrous satin dress the only sound in the quiet. The skirt wasn't long, it came just to her knees, but the generous folds of dark-green satin made sensuous sounds over her nylon-clad thighs when she walked. The neckline was a low V that tantalized rather than exposed, the sleeves were puffed and long. She had chosen the dress after much deliberation, but even now she wasn't sure she had made the right choice. She moved to the couch and absently picked up one of the velvety salmon-colored pillows, plumping it with her hands and tossing it back down. She glanced around, a frown bringing her brows together, even though the apartment was spotless. When she had come home from work, she had moved through the rooms like a demon, cleaning the house in record time as an outlet for her nervous energy. Because she *was* nervous.

She had accepted Devlin's dinner invitation almost on the dare she had seen in those brown agate eyes, but afterward, at work, reaction set in. Throughout the day she told herself repeatedly she was only going because she was a good businesswoman and she had an obligation to see Devlin Halliday as often as she could on the chance that she might learn something about his plans and tactics. But a cool inner voice of reason told her a man of Devlin's control and intelligence would never reveal information he didn't want her to know.

You want to be with him, that same inner voice whispered, *because he stirred you last night as no other man in your life ever has. . . .*

94

The doorbell interrupted her thoughts. It was Devlin, wearing a muted gray three-piece suit that made his waist look narrower and his lean legs longer and more powerful than his jogging outfit had. His hair had been combed, but the breeze from the coming storm had ruffled the dark-brown strands and he was raking a hand through it impatiently as he stepped inside.

"Hello. There's a hell of a wind out there. Must be a storm brewing." Then, as if he had done it every day of his life, he placed his hands low on her hips and pulled her forward to touch his mouth lightly to hers. It was the briefest of kisses, a feather brushing of his lips over hers, and then she was put firmly away from him.

"That's for being ready on time. Shall we go?"

Her senses still reeling from the feel of his mouth and the touch of his hands through the satin on her hipbones, she said haltingly, "If you'd like a drink, I now stock your brand of Scotch."

His eyes brightened with amusement. "That was thoughtful of you, but if you don't mind, I'd rather arrive at our destination before the heavens open." His eyes moved over her, a gleam of approval turning them darker. "That dress doesn't look as if it's waterproof. Do you have a raincoat?" She nodded and got it out of the closet behind him.

An ominous rumble of thunder provided the accompaniment to the sound of the door closing as Devlin helped her into the car. "Where's your raincoat?" she asked, letting her eyes flicker over the expensive suit he wore.

Underneath the well-fitted sleeve line, his shoulders moved upward negligently. "There's an umbrella in the back. I won't melt."

No, she didn't think he would. Inside the car he seemed very real, very alive, very male. He turned to reverse out of the parking place, throwing one arm over the seat of the car as he turned his head for a better view. His fingers brushed the collar of her coat before he straightened in the seat and looked ahead down the country road.

She was still struggling with the leap of nerves even that slight contact with him created inside her when her eyes wandered to his hands. He held the wheel easily, the long fingers spread out against the circular rim with a confidence and a male grace that made her remember the way he had touched her. He was a big man, but those fingers had a gentleness and a sensitivity that were sensually devastating. . . . She turned her head to stare unseeingly out the window.

When they arrived at their destination, she was surprised to find that he had chosen one of her favorite places, a country restaurant known for its fine cuisine that sat on a hill and had a view of the Mississippi as far reaching as her own. The first drops of rain pattered down as they dashed to the glass rotunda that served as an entryway. They were greeted courteously by a middle-aged man with a mane of white hair and shown to a secluded corner table with large floor-to-ceiling windows that offered a fantastic view. The cloudy sky, rather than being less impressive in the twilight, was more so. The churning clouds played out their battle over a pearly yellow background as they changed from gray to pewter blue to gunmetal in the twilight. The river was a shining rope of silver reflecting their turbulence. She thought ruefully that the sky might have been reflecting her turbulence as well. She was no less disturbed as she sat down across the table from Devlin Halliday and saw how the corner window with its view made the perfect backdrop for his dark hair, his lean face, and his wide shoulders.

She was handed a menu that looked like a half-size photograph album, its contents tabbed in index fashion. Appetizers, light meals, entrées, and desserts were easily chosen by the flip of a wrist with the finger held on the correct tab. She studied it with all her attention, grateful for anything to keep her eyes away from Devlin.

He suggested the steak-and-shrimp combo. She feigned some

interest but could honestly care less what she ate. With a slight smile she nodded her agreement and handed the attractive waitress her menu, thinking she had to control her thoughts or she would give herself away. Devlin was far too astute not to notice her disturbed state of mind. He didn't seem to, though; he hardly glanced at her as he ordered his Scotch and, after casually asking her preference, a glass of dry white wine for her.

When their drinks came, she picked up the goblet and sipped, hoping the cool liquid would give her courage. Thinking she needed some light conversation to divert her mind, she asked, "How did you find out about this place?"

One corner of his mouth tilted up. "I went to get a haircut."

"You did what?"

"I went to get a haircut," he repeated patiently.

"What does that have to do with finding out about the nicest restaurant around?"

He tilted his head and leaned back in his chair, one lean-fingered hand holding his drink. "If you wanted to know something in a strange town, wouldn't you ask someone at a hair-cutting salon?"

"I hadn't thought about it." She spent as little time as possible in hers, fretting during the hour it took to clip and cut her hair and keep it at its short, curly length. "It seems to me it would be easier to ask the clerk at the motel."

He shook his head. "No, the clerk will feel duty bound to recommend the motel restaurant. Or he might have a brother-in-law who runs an indifferent steak house down the street." He took a slow swallow from his glass and set it on the table. "People are more inclined to tell the truth when they are having their hair groomed."

She gave him a long, considering look. "You don't leave anything to chance, do you?" she said lightly, her fingers tracing the footed circle of her glass.

He met her eyes with a dark glance she couldn't interpret.

"People who leave things to chance are sometimes handed unpleasant surprises."

"And you don't like unpleasant surprises," she said, carefully lifting her wineglass to her lips, thinking of item four and what an unpleasant surprise it would be for him . . . if she decided to use it. She still hadn't had the courage to set the final wheels in motion.

"I have a particular aversion to unpleasant surprises," he said softly, watching her. "You haven't been planning one for me, have you?"

She lifted her chin. "I might be."

His mouth tightened. "Carolyn, there's nothing you can do. You were beaten the moment I started buying your stock."

"Was I?" she said. Even to her own ears her voice sounded strained.

Sitting lazily in the chair, he looked relaxed and at ease, but she could feel the intentness of his eyes roaming over her face. "What exactly are you planning, I wonder?" he said softly to himself, obviously not expecting her to answer.

The waiter, bearing their food on heated trays, was a welcome diversion. He set the plates down ceremoniously in front of them, inquired if there was anything else they needed, and left them.

Carolyn picked up her fork. She had just bitten into a succulent shrimp when Devlin said, "What was your mother like?"

Her enjoyment in her food vanished. "Why do you ask?" There was a coolness in her rebuttal question.

"Maybe because I want to know more about you," he countered.

"So you can figure out what I'm going to do next?"

A small smile tilted one corner of his mouth. "No," he drawled, "so my computer can figure out what you're going to do next."

Her fork clicked against her plate as she stared at him. "You fed me into a computer?"

Her surprise only amused him. "I do that with all the executives of the companies I'm interested in."

She struggled to regain her mental balance. "How . . . how do you do it?"

He seemed to enjoy her disconcertment. "I do a character profile on the subject. Certain characteristics are chosen and assayed according to their importance, which is my judgment of how dominant they are in the person's makeup. I feed the whole thing into a matrix of the computer and—"

"You . . . assign characteristics to people?"

He looked at her thoughtfully for a moment before he answered. Then he said, "Yes. That is the most unscientific part of the project, of course. I'm human, too. I may not assess the person correctly."

Curious in spite of herself, she said, "How does knowing a person's characteristics help you decide what course of action to take in approaching him?"

He gave her a lazy, considering look. "Say I'm working on the profile of a female, age twenty-nine. Certain patterns in her life-style indicate she has a strong streak of loyalty. So I plot a course of action that appeals to that loyalty, present it to the computer, and ask if the person will go for it. The computer gives me a percentage rate of acceptance."

She met his eyes steadily. "What rate of acceptance did your computer give your plan to offer me three years of guaranteed work to my employees?"

"Seventy-five percent," he said coolly. "Anything over fifty percent is a very sure bet."

A shudder went down her spine. The computer had been right. She'd accepted it immediately. "That's—inhuman."

He shook his head. "It's merely an attempt to organize human nature, which is, in reality, a very intricate set of facts. A computer is particularly suited to a task like that."

Playing for time, a peculiar sense of dread on her, she said, "How do you decide what characteristics people . . . have?"

"Observation, judgment."

"Yours?"

"And my assistant's."

"But we'd never seen each other . . ."

"There are ways to get information about people." He looked at her and laughed softly. "Don't scowl at me so. It isn't foolproof, you know. People are complex and harbor characteristics that are buried deep inside and are therefore difficult, if not impossible, to assess."

She leaned back in her chair, her own head suddenly clear, the adrenaline flowing. "You certainly zeroed in on me, didn't you?"

He didn't answer her. He seemed to be very involved in the cutting of his steak. She kept her eyes on his face, even though he wasn't looking at her. "When you were probing my psyche, did you find anything else interesting?"

He raised his eyes and met her gaze. "Besides the loyalty? Intelligence, honesty, determination. . . ."

She fought down the quick sense of pleasure his words gave. "You make me sound like a Saint Bernard."

". . . With the organization and leadership skills that brought a floundering company to its feet in two years"—a devilish gleam lit his eyes—"and a quick, hot temper no self-respecting Saint Bernard would be caught dead with."

She felt the sweet rise of pleasure his implied compliment to her business abilities gave. To stave it off she said in a dryly amused tone, "Well, they have all that brandy to keep them docile."

"Would brandy make you docile?"

His potent attraction hardly needed liquor to heighten it. With that feeling of freedom and rapport she always seemed to have with him, knowing somehow that she could say anything to him and he would understand, she said wryly, "You're a menace, Mr. Halliday." Her words were tempered with her slight smile. "Mata Hari had nothing on you."

He laughed softly. "Feeling exposed, are you?"

She met those brown eyes with fire in her own. "How would you like to be dissected by a machine?"

His eyes half-closed, he said softly, "I wouldn't mind. Would you like to borrow my computer?"

In spite of herself she smiled, a gleam of mischief in her eyes. "You bet I would."

"What prime personality characteristic would you give me?"

"Tenacity," she said without thinking.

His dark chuckle sent a tiny thrill prickling up her spine. "You make me sound like a bulldog."

"Panther would be more like it," she said unguardedly, regretting the words the moment they left her mouth, because she saw at once that her rash statement had stripped away the casual give-and-take of their business talk and reminded him of the intimacies they had shared the night before. A predatory gleam lit the dark fires behind his eyes, heightening the tension that sang along her nerves. "You feel—threatened?"

"Of course," she agreed lightly, hoping her tone didn't betray her. "You are . . . attacking me, aren't you?" She forced herself to keep her eyes fastened on his.

"By buying your company, you mean?"

"Yes, what else?"

"What else, indeed?" he said softly.

She was very much aware that she had handed Devlin a weapon when she had called him a panther. She had given away the fact that he disturbed her senses on a primitive level. He didn't say anything to press his advantage, but his eyes were far too knowing as they played over her face. She bent her head and tried to concentrate on her food, but her appetite had vanished and she was forced to lower her fork and give up the pretense of eating all together. To avoid looking at him, she picked up her wineglass and gazed out the window; but even so, Devlin's dark hair and one wide shoulder remained in her peripheral vision.

"Would you like some coffee?"

"Yes, please."

She had hoped the coffee would stave off that inevitable moment of intimacy in the car, but all too soon Devlin left several bills on the small tray and rose to help her on with her coat and walk with her out into the rain.

Inside the car he was silent. The swish of the windshield wipers and the tap of the rain on the roof created an intimate atmosphere that robbed her of words. She cast around for something to say and came up blank, her body telegraphing messages her mind didn't want to acknowledge. The closeness of his arm to hers, the smell of good male grooming heightened by the rain they had run through, the lean length of thigh that stretched next to hers on the seat, were all potent reminders of his attraction. She couldn't let him come in this time. . . .

At the open door of her apartment she turned to him and said in what she hoped was a cool tone, "Good night, Devlin."

He laughed softly, pushed her inside, and closed the door behind them both. In the next instant she was in his arms. "Is a streak of shyness one of your hidden characteristics?"

"Devlin, listen to me"—and the words that should have sounded cool came out sounding like a husky plea. His mouth had found her ear, and his tongue was tracing its outer shell. Her mind fought his subtle seduction while every nerve in her body sang with the need to melt into him and accept his kisses and caresses until they led to that final, most intimate embrace of all. "I can't . . . get involved with you."

"It's too late, honey. You're already involved with me. And you know it as well as I do." His mouth was at her cheek now, making its slow, warm way to her lips.

"No." She leaned into him to bury her face in his jacket and turn her face away from his mouth. "Go back to Miss Lawrence. She's more your type. I'm not. . . . I can't handle this."

Her words startled him. She had been so matter-of-fact about his involvement with another woman, he had thought she didn't care. But now, to hear Kristin's name on Carolyn's lips as he held her in his arms indicated a depth of involvement greater than he had dared hope. Had she been jealous after all? Encouraged, he said softly, "Yes, you can. Stop thinking about your company. There's nothing more you can do. There's only one thing that's important now and that's us, Carolyn, you and me. Let me learn about you physically as well as mentally. Let me explore that beautiful body of yours and give you the pleasure I know you're aching to take from me."

"Devlin, please. I don't want . . ." But even while she denied her own longing, her fingers curled upward and found the silky hair at the nape of his neck, and her mouth turned upward to his.

"You do want, honey," he murmured against her mouth. "I know all about your wants. . . ."

He stopped his own words by taking her mouth in a slow, sweet kiss. She was as soft and feminine and yielding in his arms as he knew she would be if she ever allowed herself to give in to her feelings. Her lips excited him as no other woman's ever had. He urged her mouth to open and give him access to that wine-scented warmth that waited beyond. A soft moan escaped her throat, the sound of it an erotic pleasure to his ears. He gathered her slender form closer, his hands anchoring her hips against his. God, he wanted her. He ached to feel complete in her arms, to lie down with her and join her body with his own.

She felt as if he were absorbing her, cell by cell. With his mouth and hands Devlin claimed more than her body, he claimed her mind and soul. His kiss created a new, deep hunger within her, a hunger that turned her into a woman she hardly recognized, a woman who needed him with a desperation that frightened her.

She thrust her hands against his chest and wrenched herself away. Her sudden resistance caught him off guard and his hands loosened involuntarily. She was free. She stepped back and tried to control her erratic breathing. As if on cue a faint rumble of thunder from the now receding storm broke the electric silence. His dark face was expressionless, but the storm clouds seemed to linger in the depths of his eyes as he watched her. Groping for something, anything, she said huskily, "I'll make tea, if you'd like some before you go."

If he fought for control, she couldn't see it. He merely tilted his head and said wryly, "If that's all you're offering, I'll take it."

He reached out to help her with her coat and it was all she could do not to flinch away from the brush of his fingers against her nape. Her body still tingled with awareness of him.

With a deftness that made her remember the day he had spent in her apartment earlier, he stepped to the entryway closet and hung up her coat. She crossed the plush carpeting and went round the snack bar to the kitchen, glad for the chance to recover her poise by filling the kettle and putting it on the stove. Devlin followed and slid onto the tall stool on the other side of the curving bar, his eyes shielded from her view by his dark lashes.

But he was watching her. She sat down on the other side of the bar, not quite across from him to allow a space for his long legs, and lifted her chin, meeting his eyes defiantly. "Why don't you say what you're thinking? Tell me I'm a scheming female who's playing games with you, leading you on."

His voice was soft, almost chiding. "If I thought that, would I still be here?"

Her blue eyes fastened on his, their pupils still dark with sexual excitement. He thought she must have the most expressive eyes he had ever seen. They were the only unguarded thing about her.

She said, "Why are you still here?"

His faint smile was disturbing. "Why do you think?"

With a show of courage she was far from feeling, she said, "There can't be anything between us, Devlin."

He shrugged. "If you say so."

She hadn't expected his nonchalance. Stung, she said sharply, "I won't be your . . . woman in LaCrosse."

He met her eyes with a dark, lazily sensual look. "Offends your sense of loyalty, doesn't it?"

The teakettle's whistle seared the silence. She battered down the whispering voice inside that told her he was beginning to know her far too well and said, "Licorice or apple spice?"

He grimaced. "Apple spice sounds the least dangerous of the two."

"Honey?"

His smile was rakish. "Yes?"

"For your tea," she said crisply, ignoring his play on the word.

"No, thanks." His eyes still held the gleam of amusement, and somehow that gleam disturbed her as much as his sensuously pleasing caresses had a moment ago. He was infinitely appealing, infinitely male, infinitely capable of handling any situation. He was marvelously mature, with an openness that she had to admire. How many men would, after a frustrating lovemaking session, be content to sit in her kitchen minutes later, teasing her and drinking her tea?

After she had set the steaming mugs on the counter and sat down again, he said, "There's something I'd like to know."

She held her breath, waiting.

"After years of being ignored by Jed, why did you decide to come with him when you were eighteen?"

She felt as if she were in a fencing match with blow after blow coming closer to her vital centers. How she had agonized over that decision. And she had been alone, totally alone, with no one to talk to.

She stared down into her teacup, unable to meet his eyes. "What makes you think I didn't jump at the chance of living with a wealthy man?"

"You didn't, did you?"

She was silent for a moment, staring down into the brown cup in front of her. "No. When he told me who he was, I didn't believe him. Later, when I did believe him, I told him to go away. I wanted nothing to do with him."

"How did he convince you he was your father?" The question was soft, empathetic.

"He . . . had some letters of my mother's. I knew they were hers the moment I read the first line. The handwriting and the phrasing were typically hers. She was a witty, wonderfully intelligent woman."

"I can believe that," he said, his eyes moving over her face. "I think she must have been someone very special to have had a daughter like you."

"Don't—say things like that."

"Why not, if they're true?" He sipped his tea carefully and then said, "Did Jed offer you a college education?"

Her eyes darkened. "In spite of the way I felt, the minute he walked into the store, I was drawn to him. Almost as if I . . . recognized him. I saw how successful he was, how keen his mind was. He belonged to another world. I realized that I would always be just where I was if I didn't get more education and train my mind to think with more depth. I knew that what I had wasn't enough. I wanted more. Much more. I wanted the same kind of success he had."

"Yes," he said in a deep, warm voice that told her he knew exactly what she meant, "you would."

She lifted her cup, and though she strove to be casual, her voice shook. "I thought I had achieved it . . . until you came along."

His brows came together in a frown. "My taking over your company doesn't negate what you've done."

"Doesn't it?" Her laugh was short and unamused. "To me it does."

"So that's why you're so . . . emotionally attached to Leisure Days."

"Anybody would be emotionally attached to something they've worked their heart out on for the last three years," she retorted hotly.

"But there's more than that involved here. Your whole image of yourself is wrapped up in that company . . ."

"That's not true."

106

". . . and that's a poor place to keep it," he finished, ignoring her interruption. The thunder rumbled one last warning mutter from the distance, but at the narrow snack bar the electricity crackled between them.

She flung words at him in counterattack. "What about your self-image, Mr. Halliday? Isn't it wrapped up in what you do? If you backed off now, you'd lose face, wouldn't you?"

"I can't back off, Carolyn," he said steadily. "No matter what I feel for you, I can't stop this takeover."

"You don't feel a damn thing for me," she cried. "I'm just a novelty, an amusing toy you want to pick up and play with while you're in the neighborhood." Her eyes flashed with anger and pride.

He stared at her. "Come around here and say that again."

Enraged, no longer thinking coherently, she jumped off the stool, rounded the snack bar, and threw herself at him, grasping the lapels of his jacket with clenched fingers, her blue eyes dark and wild. "You care nothing for me—"

He caught her in his arms and brought her satin-clad body up against his, making her instantly aware of his arousal. He made an anguished sound low in his throat, his face dark with some emotion she couldn't identify. "I'd give you your damn company back on a platter if I could." Their eyes locked in a battle of wills, and then, with a soft, desperate groan escaping his throat, he lowered his head and claimed her mouth with his.

CHAPTER SIX

His tender but totally possessive kiss sent a wild elation surging through her. It was as if she had goaded him into claiming her mouth and body in a way that would make her own resistance futile. He gave her exactly what she needed, a kiss driven by self-assurance and a passion that matched her own. Her hands moved up under his jacket, sliding over the silk of his shirt to discover the smooth muscles, the hard bone underneath.

His hands cupped her hips over the satin and did the impossible, pressed her even closer to his male body. He lifted his mouth from hers, only to murmur, "Carolyn," in a husky tone and trail his lips along the underside of her jaw down her neck to the sensitive pulse at the base.

"Please—" Whether the word was a protest or a plea, she couldn't have said. Her fingers moved restlessly over his back, discovering the shape and feel of him, wishing she could touch his naked skin instead of silk.

His hands went from her hips to the nape of her neck. Gentle fingers caught the zipper and pulled it down. Satin hissed as her dress slid over the pale-cream transparent bra and pantyhose she wore and fell to the floor. "Devlin—"

He picked her up to free her ankles from the clinging folds of satin, and an instant later she found herself being lowered to the velvet sofa. With great care he adjusted the pillows under her head.

Unable to get a word past the pounding tension in her throat, she shook her head, moving it back and forth against the velvety prison of the pillows. He caught her face between warm hands to stop the negative signal and leaned over her. His mouth took hers again, and his hands roamed over her to brush the straps of her bra down over her shoulder. The feel of his fingers just above her breasts made her gasp with pleasure into the mouth that hovered on hers.

"So sensitive," he murmured. "So responsive. All that passion kept hidden away for years . . . have you been waiting for me?"

Deftly he freed the front clasp of her bra and brushed the wisp of material aside to lift and caress the creamy fullness of her breast. She stifled a moan, her hands clinging to his shoulders. He lowered his head. His mouth on her sensitive skin was heaven, his lips and tongue teasing round the sensitive peak but not quite touching it. He was supremely in control, holding her with all the male force at his command, totally concentrating on her, his tongue savoring the underside of her breast, his hands wandering lower to trace the round abruptness of her hipbone and discover the smooth curve of her inner thigh. His touch ignited a golden fire deep within her loins. No longer able to resist the urge to pleasure him as he was pleasuring her, she tugged at his shirt. At once he lifted away from her to make the front buttons accessible.

She hesitated, her eyes dark with desire. He murmured encouragement to her, his eyes echoing the desire in her own. "Yes, honey. Undress me."

Her hands shaking, she fumbled with his tie. He didn't make a move to help her. He simply watched her, his eyes drinking in the movements of her creamy breasts as her hands worked at his throat. The warmth and masculine admiration in his gaze made her throat ache.

At last she pulled the knot free and slid the long ends out from under his collar. Her hands trembled but, driven by a far stronger force than her nervousness, she started at the top, slowly undoing the buttons one by one until his darkly furred chest was exposed. With a soft, inarticulate sound she spread her palms flat against his stomach and slid her hands up through the curling hairs, finding the masculine nipples underneath, feeling them harden against her fingers.

The slight shudder of his skin under her fingertips gave her a feline sense of satisfaction. A wanton need to know that he was as aroused as she was made her clasp his shoulders and push his shirt away. When she had freed his arms of the sleeves and the garment fell to the floor, she pulled him forward and ran her tongue up from his collar bone, swirling into the sensitive shell of his ear.

His response was immediate, the hardness of his male body surging against hers. He moved closer, his weight bearing her down into the soft cushions, his bare chest hard and firm against her softness. He looked down at her, amusement and male satisfaction gleaming from his eyes. "I've wanted this since that first night I saw you dancing next to the river," he muttered, his breath warm on her cheek. His hand played over her upper thighs, finding the sensitive core of her femininity still covered with nylon. He rubbed his palm knowingly, sensuously over it. She made a small sound of mingled protest and delight. "Please don't—"

He laughed softly. "You don't mean that. You want me, honey, and I want all of you, every last secret your lovely body hides. . . ."

Secret. She had a secret in her mind as well, a treacherous secret. Dear God. What was she doing lying here, letting him make love to her when he was her enemy, the man she had to fight? He would possess her body, and with it . . . he would take her mind and heart. She would have nothing left to fight him with. She would lose the strength to do the one thing that was her only hope to salvage her company. If she gave in to Devlin tonight, it would mean giving him everything she had worked for . . . and herself as well.

His hand moved under the waist of her hose, his fingers splay-

ing out over the smoothness of her abdomen, reaching, reaching
. . .

"No, Devlin." She pushed his seeking hand away and struggled to get up.

A frown wrinkled his forehead, pulled the dark brown brows together. "What?"

"Let go of me." She groped to refasten her bra.

"You don't mean that." He leaned forward, stopping her by clamping her against the pillows with his weight, locking her hands between their chests.

Her dark-blue eyes flashed an angry warning at him. His brown ones met hers with an imperturbable coolness. In a husky tone she said, "I've changed my mind."

He gazed at her, his face betraying nothing of his own thoughts. "Just like that?"

She struggled, trying to free her hands, but his weight didn't ease away and she was helpless. "Sometimes it happens that way." She glared up at him. "Maybe you just don't turn me on."

He smiled, but the movement of his mouth had nothing to do with amusement. "Try again." He shifted his weight, and she lifted her hands to push him away, only to feel his hard hands clamp around her wrists and draw them down to each side of her. "And make it the truth this time."

His head lowered and his mouth found her breast. With elaborate care he tongued a rosy peak to quivering hardness. An unbelievable burst of pleasure exploded deep within her. Caught on an edge of tortured delight, she forced out the words. "I don't—want this."

His tongue raked upward, found the corner of her lips, explored the curve of her mouth with butterfly lightness. "Liar."

Her body writhing with need, she turned her head into the pillows. "I can't let you make love to me."

He stared at her for a long, tension-ridden moment. Then his dark features hardened. "What's the matter, Carolyn? Are you

111

afraid you'll forget yourself in passion and reveal that devious plan you have to destroy my takeover bid?"

"I'd never tell you—" Too late she saw the trap.

"—what you're planning," he finished, his fingers loosening around her wrists. His voice coolly remote, he said softly, "So you are planning something."

"We can never be lovers," she said, the words echoing in her brain with a hollow sound.

"We already are," he said flatly, "even if we haven't quite . . . completed the act. We can't look at each other without wanting to touch and possess, and that's as true of you as it is of me." He sat up, his eyes guarded. "All right. We'll play it your way. You go ahead and do whatever it is you think you have to do." He sat for a moment, taking in the bareness of her body with a cool assessment that chilled her blood. "But take my word for it, honey, no matter what you do, your company is going to merge with mine." He paused and then said silkily, "And you are going to merge with me."

His blunt sexual promise heated her cheeks. Her temper exploding, she raised her hands and shoved them against his chest. "You can't say those things to me. I—"

He caught her hands and forced her back against the cushions, watching with pleasure as her breasts heaved with her exertion. The glitter in his eyes didn't match his soft, cool, slicing voice. "When this little corporate game of ours is over, *nothing* will stop me from taking you to bed, not your precious plots, nor your fear of having an illegitimate child, nor any other excuse your imaginative mind can manufacture. We belong together." Their eyes locked in a battle of wills. Then he loosened his hold on her, picked up his shirt, and shrugged into it with a lazy assurance that astounded her. When he had finished buttoning it, he turned his raking gaze back to her. "I wonder what it will take to make you realize that."

She slept little that night after Devlin left, and when the pale

112

rays of the morning sun lightened the drapes at her windows, she was relieved to get out of the bed that had been like a prison and get into her jogging clothes.

She drove to Pettibone Park, her pulses pounding with the thought that she might run into Devlin, her traitorous body aching for the sight of him. The park was empty, and the swift kick of disappointment in her stomach told her that far more than her body was involved with Devlin Halliday.

The painful thought forced her out of the car and into her warmup stretches. The preliminaries didn't help. Even after she started to run, she felt the tension in every muscle, tension that had accumulated over her long, sleepless night. Her feet churned automatically down the path, while her mind traveled back to the end of that soul-destroying evening. Devlin had coolly picked up his tie and jacket, finished dressing, and let himself out of her apartment without a backward glance, leaving her body aching with unfulfilled desire, her mind reeling at his abrupt departure.

How quiet and lonely the room had been after he left! How frequently a picture of him had come to her mind as she undressed for bed and slid under the covers. She had lain there, thinking that if she hadn't been so foolish, he would have been with her, in her bed, his hands and mouth and tongue cooling the fever under her skin . . . or heating it to a burning blaze.
. . .

Her sneakers hit the hard-packed sand in a faster rhythm. Should she give up? Should she stop fighting and simply hand over the company to Devlin? Certainly there was no logical reason for her to continue to resist the takeover. There was only the emotional one, her need to finish what she had started on her own, without any help or interference from anyone. If she did stop fighting, if she did simply sit back and allow the inevitable to happen and Devlin to take over her company, there would be nothing to stop her from becoming his lover. She could go to his arms freely, and know that delight of belonging to him, a delight like nothing she had ever experienced in her life. Even now, as

113

she skirted the branch that still lay in the path, her skin remembered the feel of his fingers on her arm as he had guided her around that same branch the day before.

Dear God, she couldn't even go jogging without thinking about him. It took only a harmless branch to set her remembering his effect on her senses! She was on the verge of being emotionally involved with him even though he had revealed nothing of his feelings to her. He had said they "belonged together," whatever that meant. What did it mean? A short, disastrous affair? Living together? Certainly nothing more permanent. And how could she handle the breakup that would be inevitable with a man like Devlin?

And what of the other alternative? If she resisted to the last and went ahead with her plan, he would be furious. Any attraction he felt for her would die a sudden death when he discovered what she had done. He would no longer want her. He would turn his back and walk out without a second glance just as he had last night.

And she would be safe. . . .

The pale-green collar of her dress fluttered against her neck as she opened the door to the warehouse of Ken Houston and Sons Marina.

The secretary, dressed casually in jeans and a loose-fitting top, her red hair flowing in a stream of auburn gold down her back, was bending over the second drawer of a filing cabinet when Carolyn walked in the door. The woman turned and Carolyn saw that she wore an abundance of eyeliner and eye shadow which gave her a rather hard look.

"I'm Carolyn Wakefield. I have a ten o'clock appointment with Mr. Houston."

The woman, somewhere in her late thirties, smiled, and the effect was amazing. Her face softened, and the personality behind the makeup came shining through. "Oh, yes, Miss Wakefield, Mr. Houston is expecting you. Go right on in."

She waved vaguely to her right at a metal door that showed traces of having been opened by several grimy hands.

Ken Houston sat behind his desk like a restless bear, his oversized body ensconced in a huge black leather chair of ancient vintage. The cigar clamped between his teeth gave off a pungent odor.

"Hello, Ken."

The eyes, hidden behind horn-rimmed spectacles, were cautious, waiting.

He nodded. "Carolyn." Her name was a grudging admission of her presence. His eyes played over her stylish dress, her nylon-stockinged legs, her beige closed-toe pumps. "You're looking well." He puffed on the cigar, sending a cloud of blue smoke into the air. "Not that I'm pleased to see the competition walk in my door looking so prosperous on a Thursday morning." More blue smoke filtered out of the corner of his mouth. "What can I do for you?"

Taking a breath, she said bluntly, "I was thinking more in terms of something I could do for you."

She waited, watching the keen mind ticking over under the shiny dome of his bald head. He said, "Why should you want to help me?"

"I'm in a bind," she admitted, knowing Ken Houston and everyone else in LaCrosse were probably well aware that Halliday, Incorporated, was stalking Leisure Day Houseboats. Nothing less than the truth would do if she hoped to gain Ken's help.

"Am I supposed to be unhappy about that?" Ken asked sagely.

In spite of herself Carolyn smiled. "I thought you might feel that way." She leaned back, trying to control her apprehension. "Because I am—in this bind, I have a proposition to make you."

The corners of his mouth tilted as he shifted the cigar to the other side. "I'm all ears." He tipped the chair back and watched her with a wary interest.

"I'd like to offer you the first chance to a year's lease on my

115

dock. It would be a nonrevocable lease offered to you at the cost of one dollar."

His chair snapped forward. "Are you serious?"

She reached into the slim briefcase she carried. "I have the contract all drawn up, if you'd like to look at it." She rose from the chair and handed the papers across his desk to him.

He adjusted his glasses farther down his nose, read for a moment, and then glanced up at her. After he had scrutinized her features for what seemed like a very long time, he tossed the papers down on the desk. "What in God's name possessed you to offer me this?"

"You know Halliday's after me."

He nodded.

"He wants the dock. I don't want him to have it. It's that simple."

"You can't operate without access to the river."

She lifted her chin. "I know that."

"You're sabotaging your own outfit."

"I know that, too."

Ken Houston leaned back, his eyes narrowing. "What happens to your employees if you sell your company up the river?"

Carolyn's temper flared, but she controlled it and said coolly, "I have an ironclad agreement that they are to be employed for three years after the date of the merger."

Ken squinted down at the contract. "Who drew up this document?"

"My lawyer and I did. It's watertight."

"Even against the high-flown legal brains Halliday can afford to employ?"

Carolyn lost her hold on her temper. "Suppose they do break it. For the cost of one lousy dollar you will have had the use of the dock during the time it takes them to file suit!"

He leaned forward and planted his large forearms on the desk. "Young lady, when you get as old as I am, you'll learn that the things that come the cheapest end up costing the most money.

116

I can't afford to get involved in litigation with some high-powered attorney from New York City over something I didn't want in the first place."

"A year ago you wanted that dock," Carolyn said grimly.

"Only because I thought it would slow you down considerably to have to erect a new one."

Through gritted teeth, she said, "You won't sign the lease, then?"

He stared at her, animosity crackling though the lenses of his glasses. Then, in a sudden quick movement, he picked up the pen lying on his desk and flipped through the pages of the contract to the final one. He signed his name with a scratching scrawl.

"There are three copies," she said, reaching into her briefcase and handing more papers across to him, the blood pounding through her head at his sudden capitulation and the thought that now that it was done, there was no turning back. "Please sign all of them."

"I must be out of my ever-loving mind," he grumbled, taking the papers from her and shuffling through them to find the proper page to sign.

"You have nothing to lose and everything to gain." Her voice was far cooler than she felt.

He tossed the papers back at her. "When does this lease take effect?"

"The moment I sign." She took the slim black pen out of her case and quickly added her name in the blank below Houston's.

"This is your copy. If you'd like to have one notarized, I can prepare another set."

He took the cigar out of his mouth and waved at her impatiently with it. "Forget it. We both know we're who we say we are. I'll be surprised if that paper's worth the powder to blow it to hell, anyway, when Halliday gets through with it."

"My lawyer has assured me of its veracity. Even if Halliday does take over, he's still required by law to honor any contracts

117

made before the merger." She rose and picked up the extra contracts to tuck into her case.

"You got any houseboats tied up to that dock now?"

She raised her head to look at him. "No. A customer took delivery on a boat yesterday. The dock is clear."

"I'll expect it to stay that way."

"It will," she said, snapping her case closed. She turned to go.

"Carolyn."

At the door, she turned. "Yes?"

He replaced his cigar, his eyes raking over her slender figure. "Aren't you forgetting something?"

"I don't think so."

He drew out his wallet, extracted a bill, and tossed it on the desk to her. She was filled with an overwhelming urge to walk out the door and leave it there.

Astutely, he said, "The contract isn't legal until I pay the fee."

Her head high, she walked to the desk and picked up the bill, shoving it into her purse without looking at it.

She turned to go, but once again he said her name.

She faced him. "Yes?"

"Good luck." Around his cigar he smiled faintly, a movement his lips seemed to find strange.

An answering smile tilted her mouth. "Thanks. I'll need it." *Especially when I tell Jed what I've done.*

Jed was livid. He sat behind the bar in his house that evening and roared into the big room, "You did what?"

"I gave Houston a lease on the dock."

His face was suffused with a dull red color. "What did you do a damn fool thing like that for?"

"Because I had to. I had to stop Halliday."

Jed lifted his glass to his lips, swallowed deeply, and set the tumbler on the bar with a thump. "What makes you think this will stop him?"

"He doesn't want my company. He only wants that dock."

118

Jed's lips lifted in a knowing smile. "I don't think that's all he wants."

She pretended not to understand. "Is he . . . are you seeing him this evening?"

Jed shook his head. "He left. Flew to Chicago. And from there he was going to Greece, I think."

"Greece?"

"He has his finger in pies all over the world, a little shipping here, a little mining there."

Tipping her head down, staring into the clear white wine Jed had given her, she murmured, "He's come a long way from 'The Silken Tent.' "

"What?"

"A Robert Frost poem Devlin taught when I was in his class." Carolyn's fingers traced around the stem of her glass. She didn't add, as she might have, that the poem was a lushly sensual one, and that Devlin's reading of it had haunted her nights for a long time. "How well do you know him?"

"Not as well as you do, I bet."

Her response was quick, too quick. "I don't know him at all."

Jed chuckled. "Don't try to pull the wool over my eyes, girl. He's interested in you—and your eyes turn dark as sapphires when he's around." He gave her a narrow-eyed, searching look. She did her best to meet that look with her own face smooth, her eyes guarded. Watching her like a hawk, he added softly, "I'd like to see you two get together. He'd be a damn fine catch for any woman."

"So is a Mississippi catfish," she said dryly, hoping to throw Jed off the track by mentioning his favorite prey.

Jed threw his head back and laughed. "You never could land one of those, either, as I remember."

Forcing her thoughts away from Devlin, she remembered how, during her first few months with Jed, he had taken her fishing. And, as he had in every other aspect of her life, he demanded perfection from her. She couldn't cast to suit him, and

119

she managed to snag her line almost every time. She had finally opted to save her nerve and temper and had urged him to go fishing alone just as he had before her arrival.

She twirled her wineglass thoughtfully around on the bar. "Did he ever mention anything to you about why he quit teaching and took the plunge into the corporate world?"

"Didn't have to. I know why he did it."

She looked up, her curiosity sharpened. "You do?"

"It doesn't take a genius to figure it out. Money, girl. College professors make damn little."

"The Devlin I knew eight years ago wasn't the type to be motivated by money."

Jed cast a shrewd, knowing look over her. "He hadn't lost his wife then, either."

"His wife?"

Jed closed his eyes. "I'd guess he felt guilty about his wife's death."

"Why would he feel—guilty?"

Jed squinted at her. "Maybe because he didn't have enough money to provide for his wife's health care."

Carolyn's stomach churned. "I—what makes you say that?"

Jed's eyes fell. "Guilt is a great motivator."

Carolyn stared at him in the silence, and behind him, Elizabeth's portrait smiled into the room. Yes, Jed would know about guilt.

She didn't know what to say, so she kept silent, her fingers tracing a line of moisture on the cool glass.

Jed hunched his shoulders and seemed to pull himself back from wherever his thoughts had taken him. He lifted his head to look at her. "Do you like him?" The question was wry, probing.

Like? What a pale word to describe the feelings Devlin aroused. But she couldn't let Jed know how much Devlin disturbed her and raise false hopes. Striving for a casualness she didn't feel, she moved her shoulder under the silky green dress

120

as if she hadn't thought about it at all. "He's tall, dark, and devastating. What's not to like?"

Jed tilted the glass to his lips, then set it down and gave her a straight look. "He might be too forceful for a female with my blood in her veins, I'm thinking."

"You think too much," she said blandly.

"That's what your mother used to tell me." The reference to his relationship to her mother was rare, and his words sent a shiver through her. As if he sensed her emotional reaction, he gave her a strange, reflective look. "You're not getting any younger."

Glad to be off the subject of her mother, she said crisply, "The next thing, you'll be telling me you want grandchildren."

He took refuge behind a mock offended air. "Why should I be any different from anyone else? Of course I want grandchildren."

She lifted the wineglass and looked straight into his eyes across the top of it. "That would be difficult, wouldn't it, since you have no children."

He polished off the rest of his drink and slammed the glass on the bar. "I intend to acknowledge you as my daughter soon, Carolyn."

She thought of the sensational publicity his revelation would generate and said soberly, "Jed, I don't want that."

He shook his head. "I do. I've made up my mind. As soon as I've told Donna, I'll make a public announcement."

She hadn't been aware of holding her breath, but now something seemed to collapse inside her. "Don't do this, Jed. There's too much at stake. Your business association with Matthew, Donna's attitude . . ."

"I'll talk to her tomorrow and announce it before the week is out."

Carolyn felt the glass tremble in her hands. She brought it down to the polished wood surface. "Are you serious?"

"Never more so." His tone was even and all trace of amusement had disappeared.

"But if Donna uses her influence to urge Matthew to sell out—"

"She won't."

"How can you be so sure now when for years you've worried —"

"I'm a poker player, sweetie. And right now it just feels right. The cash flow indicates I'm in the strongest position I've ever been. Donna's got more to lose by ending her husband's association with me than I have. Even if Matthew did pull out, I'd survive."

She lifted her head and stared at him across the top of the bar. Blue eyes exactly like her own met hers. "Why, Jed? Why now, after all these years?"

His silvery lashes flickered down. "I think we've both been punished long enough, don't you?"

Her throat full, she looked down at the highly polished wood of the bar, more conscious than ever of the full-length portrait of Jed's wife, Elizabeth, fair, fragile Elizabeth, who had been crippled in an auto accident and clung to her thread of life with a tenacity and a cheerfulness that kept Jed from divorcing her and living the life of a normal man.

"Nothing can change what happened," she said huskily, reciting the litany she had first composed when she was eighteen and had learned that her father was not dead as her mother had told her all her life, that her father was alive, that he had had a long, passionate affair with her mother that ended only after her mother had discovered she was pregnant.

"I've never been sorry you were born," he said in a choked tone. "I've only been sorry that I didn't have the courage to claim you as my own long before this." In a rare show of physical affection he reached out and covered her hand with his. "I'm proud, very proud of you. I want the world to know you're my daughter."

The warmth of his hand over hers brought the swift rush of tears to the back of her eyes. "Thank you, Jed."

He tightened his grip. "But I don't agree with what you've done on this merger battle. Whatever possessed you to offer that dock to Houston?"

She laughed, her amusement mingled with tears and a fatalistic realization that her father would never change. Jed's brief excursion into emotionalism was over. It was back to the business at hand.

As they went into dinner, he continued to badger her about the dock until at last, after several minutes of listening to his tirade on what he considered to be her departure from sanity, she laid her fork down on her plate and said in an exasperated tone, "Jed, it's done. I can't undo it now."

"Then you can do the honest thing and notify Devlin that the dock is no longer a part of Leisure Days's property."

A nerve did a dance in her stomach. "Why should I do that?"

"Dammit, because he—" He stopped suddenly, his face red with intensity, his mouth half-open. He swallowed once, blinked. "Because he's been honest with you, that's why." Whatever he had been about to say, it wasn't that. "You can return the favor."

"I'm not obligated by law to tell him anything."

"No, you're not obligated by law," Jed said harshly, "but you should be obligated by your conscience."

He was right, she knew. Jed was scrupulously honest in all his dealings, saying it was much easier that way. It was one of the things she admired about him. She poked at her salad, stirring the green leaves around in the wooden bowl. "My conscience has nothing to do with it."

"If you think that, you haven't learned anything from me in these past twelve years."

"Jed—"

"Being honest gives you the freedom to feel you have the right to success. Without that feeling, you're dead," he said heavily, "or you might as well be. Besides, if Halliday doesn't know about your little rental scheme, he won't give up. And that's really what you had in mind, isn't it?"

"Yes." Her voice was a soft whisper in the room.

"Then, give him a chance to save face at least. Tell him, so he can pull back and make an announcement to the stockholders that he's no longer interested in purchasing the company."

Her appetite gone, she stared at Jed. "I'll call him tomorrow."

He shook his head. "Wait a week. He should be back from Greece by then. I'll give you his number."

Around midnight eight days later, in the bedroom of a luxurious suite in the Plaza, a high-rise hotel overlooking the Loop in Chicago, Milt tossed a newspaper into Devlin's lap. He sat slumped in the gold velvet chair beside the bed, his long, jean-clad legs stretched out before him. He looked up, tugged at the neck of his dark-brown sport shirt, and straightened to pick up the paper, his lean frame settled more deeply into the cushions. It was a Friday-morning copy of the Milwaukee *Herald Tribune*.

"Thought you might be interested in a story in the 'State' section," Milt said, a gleam of amusement in his eyes.

Devlin pushed aside the sheaf of papers that surrounded him, the cost flow sheet and list of assets of the California-based Electronic-Tech company that Milt thought might be worth looking at, and picked up the paper, turning to the inside section. He saw the picture at once. The photographer had caught Carolyn in profile next to Jed. Her classic features and slim figure were as beautiful as ever but she looked strained and not like herself. Jed's smile was wide as he beamed into the camera full face. Devlin scanned the article quickly. "So he finally acknowledged her as his daughter," he murmured.

Milt's sandy brows rose to a peak. "You knew?"

"I knew."

"That changes things, doesn't it. Lang will surely buy a controlling interest in the stock and stop us from—"

Devlin tossed the paper to the coffee table and shook his head. "If Jed was going to save her, he'd have done it before this. Jed

124

believes in letting people make their own mistakes."

"You're still going after Leisure Days, then?"

"Yes." Devlin's eyes strayed back to the picture. She was as self-possessed and beautiful as he remembered. He'd wondered. In Greece he'd swum in the Aegean Sea, thinking it was not the same shade of blue as her eyes. It was more turquoise. But the sky over the Acropolis . . . now, that had been the right color. In the sunlight it had been the same brilliant sapphire.

He remembered the morning he'd been swimming in the motel pool. A woman had approached him, a successful advertising executive, in Athens on business. She'd been stunning, witty, intelligent. She was well read, her mind occupied with things other than her own looks and career. Under normal circumstances she was a woman he would have been interested in seeing a great deal more of. But he had avoided her that night, and checked out the next day without calling her. His thoughts were too full of a dark-haired witch dressed in green satin . . . and later, undressed. . . . He wanted to see Caro, be with her, hear her talk, touch her skin. He tossed the cost sheet on top of the newspaper. If he called his pilot and packed, he could be in LaCrosse in an hour. . . .

The phone buzzed impatiently, and Devlin cursed under his breath. He was annoyed by the interruption. He had thought he was safe from its clanging summons for tonight at least. Few people knew he was back in town. He gave Milt a disgruntled look and got up to walk to the bedside table and pick up the phone.

"Hello."

The short, irritated tone of his voice echoed back in his ear through a long silence. He must have given the caller second thoughts about answering.

Then a low, feminine voice said, "This is Carolyn. Am I . . . interrupting something?"

That familiar husky quality of her voice gave him a kick of

pleasure. Where had she gotten his number? And why was she calling at this hour?

"Nothing that can't wait," he said coolly.

There was another little silence and just as he realized what nighttime activity she thought he was engaged in, she said, "I . . . need to talk to you."

He sat down on the bed and hoisted his legs up, stretching his long frame out into a semblance of comfort. "I'm listening"—aware that Milt was trying to disguise his interest. Lifting the receiver away, he said, "It's Carolyn Wakefield."

Milt's eyebrows flew up.

She said hesitantly, "There's someone with you."

"Yes," he said, perversely not identifying Milt.

"I—thought you might be in bed."

A smile of wicked amusement lifted his lips. "I am."

The silence that followed told him his shot had gone home. "I'd really rather not talk to you over the phone." Her cool tone brought a smile to his lips. She went on, "I thought if you were returning to LaCrosse soon, we might . . . have dinner together."

Even though she believed he was in bed with another woman, she was asking him to spend the evening with her. His curiosity grew. "Is the topic of this discussion business . . . or personal?"

"Business, of course."

"Of course," he said mockingly, lying back against the head of the bed, his quick mind moving like lightning. On first impulse he opened his mouth to say he'd be there in the morning. He'd already decided to go before her call. But a corner of his mind whispered caution. If he could get her to agree to come here, he could have her in Chicago in two hours or three at the most. And she'd be off her home ground . . . and perhaps off balance as well.

"I wasn't planning to come to LaCrosse any time in the near future."

The silence that followed his blunt words was satisfying. She must have really wanted to see him. He hoped he hadn't made a mistake. Suppose she stopped negotiating and hung up. "I see," came the husky answer into his ear. "You wouldn't have any time within the next week. . . ."

"Why don't you come here for a few hours?" he suggested with a casual nonchalance. "It's Friday night. I could have my plane there for you in fifty-five minutes."

"If that's the case, then you could . . . come here."

"I have a meeting scheduled at this hotel tomorrow morning at nine o'clock."

She paused, tried again. "Doesn't your pilot have better things to do than fly around in the middle of the night?" She was stalling for time now, he realized, trying to think before she made a definite decision.

"That's what I pay him for." He let a faint amusement creep into his voice.

"I really don't think it's necessary for me to . . ."

"Tonight is the only free time I'll have for the next two weeks."

She was silent.

"If you're on a tight schedule, you can stay for an hour, or for as long as it takes us to complete our discussion. Bob will be waiting to fly you back whenever you say the word."

"Another poignant silence. "All right."

Her capitulation gave him a sting of pleasure like nothing he'd experienced in years. He grinned triumphantly at Milt, but his voice into the receiver to Carolyn was coolly offhand. "Shall we say . . . one thirty?"

"Make it two o'clock," she countered.

"Two o'clock it is," he said, and hung up before she had the chance to say she'd changed her mind.

He cradled the phone and looked across at Milt. The other man grinned. "Does this mean I get the evening off?"

"What do you think?" Devlin pushed himself off the bed and grasped the hem of his sport shirt to pull it over his head, all the weariness and irritation he'd felt a moment ago gone. He'd have to take a shower, order flowers and wine, make arrangements for breakfast. Whistling, he unzipped his jeans and headed for the bathroom. Milt, a broad smile on his face, let himself out of the hotel suite, stifling his own urge to whistle in consideration for the other tenants on the fourteenth floor.

CHAPTER SEVEN

It was like stepping into a surrealistic time zone, driving to the airport in the middle of the night, watching the pilot come walking toward her out of the dark, having him help her board the sleek Learjet that bore the words HALLIDAY, INCORPORATED, on the smooth underbelly near the wing. Inside, the lights from the control panel gave the pilot's face an eerie reflection. Bob Hanson was not at all what she expected. He was friendly, rotund, and well past forty. He managed to say just enough to make her feel at ease as she slid into the comfortable leather chair behind him and strapped herself in.

They lifted off into a dark sky. From the ground the stars had been partially obscured by gray clouds, but as the plane ascended, the clouds fell away and the stars were brilliant and close.

She sat back and tried to relax and shut out the thoughts of the confrontation that awaited her at her destination. Whatever Devlin's reaction was, in two hours from now, perhaps less, it would be over, and she would be back in this seat and on her way home.

She barely had time to adjust to the smoother feel of high-altitude flight when Bob called to her that Chicago was below them. "We'll probably circle O'Hare longer than it took us to get here," he said wryly.

Even so, within a short time they were on the ground. Bob insisted on following her into the lobby of the huge airport complex to guide her out to the car that Devlin had provided for her, saying that Mr. Halliday had given him his instructions, and he intended to follow them.

Another bland-faced man who seemed to have no curiosity about the woman who was going to see Devlin Halliday in the middle of the night sat behind the wheel of the black Mercedes. He drove without making any attempt at conversation until he pulled up in front of the hotel. "Mr. Halliday is waiting for you in suite four. You'll find it on the fourteenth floor. The elevator is to your left as you go in."

She thanked him, and clutching her shoulder bag to her hip and wishing she had never agreed to come, she climbed out of the luxurious depths of the car.

Ablaze with spotlights from both above and below, the green canvas canopy over the entrance fluttered in the Chicago breeze. The night was warm, but a chill prickled over her arms. She was glad she had worn the nubby cotton beige jump suit with its matching jacket. She fingered a wooden button at her waist nervously as she climbed the steps.

Her head high, she opened the door and crossed the tasteful dark-green carpeting. She reached for the call button, and almost at once the door opened noiselessly in front of her. She stepped inside and was delivered to the correct floor, the door sliding open again to reveal the vista of an elegant hallway carpeted in beige, its walls papered with an expensive, grass-cloth paper. There were only four doors in the hall, and a quick glance showed her that number one was just to her left. She walked to the last door. In a state of numbed tension, her heart pounding, she raised her hand and depressed the small lighted bell.

In the silence her heart continued its loud drumbeat. *It will all be over in an hour.* She repeated the thought as though it were a litany, knowing it was all she had to sustain her.

The door swung open. Devlin, a faint smile on his face, stood just inside, his body indolently relaxed, his hand reaching out for hers. "Hello."

He drew her inside, his fingers warm and possessive over hers, and all her defenses collapsed. She had missed him. How incredible. She hadn't seen him for eight days and now the sight of him was infinitely satisfying. He was dressed casually, in a long-sleeved shirt in a midnight shade of blue, its buttons open halfway down his chest, the sleeves rolled back over his forearms and denim pants that looked as if they had been welded to his lean hips and muscular thighs.

"Can I take your jacket for you?"

She shook her head, but he was already slipping his fingers under the strap of her purse and sliding her jacket over her shoulder. "It seems I have no choice," she said, aware of the husky breathiness in her voice that was the reaction of her body to his brief touch.

He hung her jacket in the closet, his face cool. While she stood helplessly watching, he moved across the pale-beige rug and walked up two steps to a dining area where a small drinks-table had been set up against one wall under a lithograph of a huge, opulent white rose. The flower provided a backdrop for Devlin's dark head, its petals spreading above him in an erotic lushness. "What would you like to drink?"

"I really didn't plan to stay that long."

His mouth curved in a smile. "How long can it take to have a drink?"

She thought of what she had to tell him and said, "I'll take some white wine, if you have it."

He nodded, turned his broad back to her to fix their drinks, and seconds later returned carrying her wineglass and his own drink, a short glass she supposed contained his Scotch. He descended the two steps and it was then she noticed he was barefoot. His feet were like the rest of him, tanned, lean, well formed. The sight of them shouldn't have disturbed her. It did.

"Sit down." He nodded at the russet sectional couch surrounding a square glass table. He leaned over the table and set their drinks on it.

She choose the side chair that seemed reasonably safe. He

walked round the table and sat in the middle of the couch, leaving two feet of space between them, holding his glass while he stretched out his legs and got comfortable.

The silence seemed to ring in her ears. "This wine is very good," she said, after she had sipped a bit.

"I'm glad you like it," he replied amiably, making her grit her teeth with his seemingly limitless show of patience. His bland unconcern, his cool confidence that nothing she had to say could be too disconcerting, grated on her nerves.

She set her glass down on the table, braced herself, and said, "I'm here because I . . . have something to tell you."

He gave her an amused, knowing look over the top of his glass. "That kind of a loaded preamble generally leads into the line 'I'm pregnant.' But that's not the case with you, is it?"

She struggled to maintain a hold on her temper. "I've already told you this was a business matter."

"Ah, yes, a business matter." He looked at her with a bland, unconcerned smile. "Somehow," he said softly, "I didn't think you'd come all this way in the middle of the night to talk shop."

His nonchalance goaded her. No longer caring what his reaction was to her news, she met his eyes steadily and said in a low voice, "I've leased the dock to a competitive concern."

His only sign of surprise was a slight narrowing of the eyes. "For how long?"

"A year." She sat waiting for the explosion. In the silence she watched him, waiting for something, anything. What would it be? A violent lunge toward her, a red-faced apoplectic explosion, hands wrapped round her throat?

He set his glass down on the table and turned his head to gaze at her, his features unchanged from the look of bland amusement he had worn a moment ago. "Now, I wonder why it didn't occur to me you might do that?"

Still barely able to believe his cool acceptance, she said huskily, "Your computer failed you."

"My computer isn't to blame. It can only analyze the facts I

132

put into it. It can't generate new ones. That's up to me. I'm the one with cotton wool in my head." In the face of his calm, mature acceptance of blame for his error, she felt lost. She had braced herself for a flaming argument, recriminations, or silent rage. She gathered her scattered wits and said what she had come to say. "I'm prepared to buy your stock back from you at thirty percent above market price."

"Are you, indeed?" he murmured, his eyes flickering away from hers to stare down at the drink he held in his long-fingered hands. He sat that way, letting the silence stretch until she wanted to scream. Why was he hesitating? Surely he didn't want her company now. He had no reason to want it.

"Suppose"—his voice was soft, reflective—"suppose I don't want to sell."

She rose up away from the back of the sofa, her skin tingling with alarm. "But you must," she cried. "You have no reason to want Leisure Days now—"

"Oh, I have a reason," he interrupted her softly.

"You can't possibly. You wanted the dock. The dock is gone."

"Yes," he murmured, "but you aren't."

She stared at him, her eyes dark. "What is that supposed to mean?"

"Maybe I want to become . . . your employer."

"My employer? That's impossible. I'll resign my position."

"You do, and I'll rescind my agreement to secure your peoples' employment for three years."

"You can't—do that. Our agreement stated—"

"If you remember," he said carefully, "I haven't signed it yet."

She stared at him, her mouth open. She had signed the papers and returned them to him. She had assumed he would sign them immediately and put them in the mail to her. She had made a gross tactical error, not insisting that those papers be returned by express mail before she had impulsively agreed to jump on the plane and come to Chicago. She had been too eager. She had wanted to see him, even though she knew he had just come from another woman's arms. . . .

Anger and jealousy and a deep, primitive rage swept through her. "You can't have my company!" She lunged at him, her hands raised to strike. Her sudden attack took him by surprise, the slight weight of her body throwing him back against the cushions. In a quick, reflexive move of self-defense he braced himself and brought his arms up to block her attack, catching her wrists and twisting her arms to the side away from his face. "For God's sake, Carolyn!"

She writhed in his arms like a spitting cat, her frustration and anger making her kick out at him with her feet. One wildly aimed thrust caught him just below the knee. He muttered an oath and trapped her legs with his own, forcing her back against the cushions with his body. "Listen to me, you wildcat."

She shook her head, her eyes dark and wild, her body registering the hard length of him pressed on her. "I've listened to you long enough. You're nothing but a liar and a cheat."

"And what are you?" he asked smoothly, his hands tightening, his eyes glittering with the first show of emotion she had seen since she walked into his apartment. "Little Miss Clean from the prairie? Always scrupulously honest?"

"I came to tell you what I'd done . . ."

"So that I would let you buy back your stock," he finished smoothly. "Hardly an altruistic motive."

"You can't possibly want to buy into Leisure Days now."

He leaned over her, his dark face breaking into a smile. "You should have taken my offer of using my computer to analyze me, honey. You said yourself my outstanding quality is tenacity. The computer would have told you your scheme had a fifteen percent or less chance of success."

Her temper flared out of control. "I don't need a computer to analyze you," she said, emotion making her voice husky. "You're nothing but a cheap opportunist with the morals of a tomcat."

134

His pupils flared dangerously, and his grip tightened on her wrists until she cried out. "You self-righteous little hypocrite." Then his eyes narrowed, and he gave her that familiar speculative look, as if he were rewinding her words inside his head to replay them at a different speed and getting an entirely different interpretation of them. "You *were* jealous, weren't you?"

"Jealous?" The word was scathing, contemptuous. She glared up at him. "I could never be jealous of the women who shared your bed. I couldn't keep track of them all."

"Most of them are figments of your imagination."

"The one tonight wasn't."

"You asked if I was with someone. You didn't specify male or female."

"You said you were in bed."

"It's the most convenient place to sit since it's next to the phone."

"I don't believe you."

He gazed at her for a moment longer. Then, in a swift, graceful move, he let go of her wrists and levered himself away, freeing her from the burden of his weight. On the cushion beside her, he straightened, his face a cool mask. "Don't, then. That's your privilege."

His casual unconcern stung. It also convinced her he was telling the truth. She sat up and tugged at her jump suit, telling herself she had been a complete fool. She had been jealous and she'd given herself away. She would have to repair the damage somehow by convincing him that he was wrong in thinking that she cared about what he did.

"Naturally it's none of my business," she said coolly. "I just didn't want to feel guilty thinking that I had deprived you of your evening's entertainment."

"Is that really the way you feel?"

"Yes, of course. I—"

"Then, stay," he said softly, "and provide alternative amusement."

Slowly the color that had made her cheeks brilliant during their altercation returned to flicker under her skin. "One-night stands aren't my thing."

"There's no reason it has to be a one-night stand," he said softly.

"No," she shook her head.

"Live with me, Carolyn."

Her ears, her skin, her heart, reacted to his words as if they had been touched by an electric wire. "I—can't."

"Why not?"

She lifted her head and met his gaze head-on. "You know why not."

"Because you might have a child?" His lips lifted. "There are ways to prevent that from happening."

"Ways that are notoriously unreliable," she said.

His lips lifted in a slight, sardonic smile. "If you become pregnant—I'll marry you."

She reacted as if he had hit her. "Oh, thanks a lot. That's a real comfort."

"Or," he said carefully, his eyes closed slits, "we could just go ahead and get married now and save ourselves the worry."

She stared at him, disbelief mingled with distaste mirrored on her face. "Now, there's a romantic proposal for you."

"Would you prefer it if I got down on one knee?"

"I'd prefer it if you'd take a running jump into Lake Michigan."

He sat back, his eyes moving lazily over her. "You're not getting any younger. Are you going to stay celibate and single for the rest of your life?"

"Now you sound like Jed," she said dryly. With a lift of her chin she gave him a straight look. "I suppose I will . . . unless, at some future point in time, I fall madly in love."

"I wonder if that could possibly happen," he murmured.

She said hotly, "Do you think I'm incapable of love?"

136

"I think you're incapable of trust," he replied quickly, "and one is impossible without the other."

"I don't trust you," she said candidly. "But fortunately there are other men around."

"Unfortunately," he said, leaning back against the cushion, "they all belong to the same male species your father does. And you learned very early he wasn't to be trusted, didn't you?"

She shook her head. "Sorry to disappoint you. My mother told me he was dead."

"But you found out he wasn't, didn't you? Right at the time a young female begins to think seriously about the opposite sex."

"I ought to be stretched out on the couch, staring at the ceiling while you take notes on a little pad."

"All I'm asking is that you think about it."

She cried, "I could think about it until I was ninety and it still wouldn't change the way I feel about you."

"Then maybe I'll have to try something else."

He moved toward her with startling swiftness, his hands catching her shoulders and forcing her back into the cushions, his mouth claiming hers with an utter surety. She was shocked into submission, taking what he had to give like a slave girl unable to defend herself. Then, in the space of a microsecond, everything changed. Her mouth responded to his assault with a flaming need as great as his own. The short week away from him had intensified her body's longing for his touch and kiss, and it now would not be denied the satisfaction it craved. She realized she had been waiting for this moment since she walked in the door. His lips softened and cajoled, his tongue came searching her honeyed depths, his hands roamed over her back, lifting her toward him, clasping her closer until her breasts were pressed against the hardness of his chest. He lifted his mouth and murmured to her in a soft, low voice totally unlike the one he had used a moment ago, "God, you're a sweet little spitfire, incredibly warm and soft and right for me." His mouth brushed over her cheek to the lobe of her ear and his tongue found the tiny, sensitive space behind it.

A fireburst of desire sprang up from deep within her and settled in the pit of her stomach, a clamoring emptiness that begged for fulfillment. His fingers moved to the top of her jump suit, and a button slipped away from its place, and then another. His fingers curved over her warm flesh unfettered by the confines of a bra. At the discovery his breathing quickened. "You want me, honey," he murmured in the ear he had just stroked with the moist tip of his tongue. "You know you do. Give yourself to me. Give me all of you, just as you are with all your lovely complexities. . . ."

"No, Devlin . . ." But her hands moved upward under his shirt and gloried in the feel of his bare flesh. She ached with the languid need to lie back and let him explore her entire body. She wanted to let her bones melt into the hardness of his body, let her mind register the pleasure of Devlin's hard thighs nudging her own.

He marveled at the soft pliancy of her body, the eager way her hands explored his back. In one instant she had gone from a spitting termagant to a willing woman, and the thought of possessing her went to his head like no alcohol ever had. He was no longer capable of doing the sane logical thing and pulling away. Driven by instinct more than experience, he traced her lips lightly with his tongue, listened to her faint gasp of pleasure, and felt the surge of response in his own body.

When she thought his errant tongue must know every crevice of her lips to perfection and would demand entrance, he unexpectedly trailed his mouth down over her throat. Easing her jump suit over her bare shoulder with his hand, he traced his tongue along her collarbone and across to the sensitive center just above her feminine curves. The rosy crest of her breast below his chin tautened with expectancy and desire. He lifted her slightly, his mouth still warm against her, and pushed the other shoulder of her jump suit down her arm. When he released her, she lay bare to the waist in his arms, her dark hair a tousled cloud of black satin against the russet cushion, the air cool against skin warmed by a fire within.

She felt as if his mouth and tongue were worshiping her body. He explored the circumference of her breast, tantalizing her with forays that stopped just short of that waiting center. She raked her fingers up to his nape, impatiently threading through the silky texture of his hair. Calm, reasonable thought was gone. Logic was gone. Fear was gone. Nothing remained but the desire to give herself to this man she loved so desperately.

His mouth skirted closer, teased, and fell away, his tongue caressing a rounded, creamy slope instead of the bud that ached for his possession. She moaned softly, thinking she had waited all her life for this and she couldn't wait any longer.

"Lift up, honey," he murmured in her ear, and mindlessly she did as he asked. As she arched toward him, he brought her suit down over her hips and legs and pulled it from under her feet to toss it away. His hand under her back urged her upward once again, and as she obeyed the command and arched toward him, his mouth came down on her in a totally surprising, utterly devastating capture of her nipple. She cried out in sheer delight, and his mouth and tongue tightened gently, making her burn with an exquisitely erotic pleasure that swelled up from deep within like a riptide to sweep all sane thoughts away.

He lifted his head and his grip loosened, and she protested with a softly spoken "No, please—"

"Patience, honey." He stripped her one remaining minuscule garment away and then shrugged out of his shirt. His denims and briefs followed in short order. She was powerless to move toward him, powerless to protest, powerless to deny the desire that raged in her like a fever. She could only lie back and admire his male beauty with a sense of gratification. He was as beautiful as she had known he would be, broad shoulders tapering to a narrow waist, flat, hard stomach, long, muscular thighs covered lightly with coal-black hair.

139

In those few seconds it took him to undress, cool logic began to whisper in her mind. She shouldn't be here. She shouldn't let him make love to her. She shouldn't . . . he came down beside her and covered her mouth with his, the warmth of his body encompassing hers, taking away the coolness, the doubt. Now, as his hands and mouth took their pleasure of her body, there were new sensations, the roughness of his hair-crisp thighs brushing against hers, the rounded curve of his hipbone bumping her own.

His fingertips feathered over her, exploring her waist, her hips, her navel. For a moment he hesitated, his body half-raised over hers, his eyes on her face. "Carolyn." His voice husky, his eyes crackling pools of brown fire, he whispered a soft love word of possession, his hand moving lower to find that intimately feminine, utterly sensitive core. She felt her breath leave her body in a betraying sound.

He murmured to her. "Let yourself feel the pleasure, honey. Don't hold back." His mouth moved over her throat, settled in the curve of her neck, brushed down across her breasts, and made her shiver with the double onslaught of delight. "It's not easy to let yourself feel all the things I can make you feel, is it? But you're doing beautifully, darling."

"Devlin, I . . . don't want to just take from you. Let me share the pleasure with you. Let me touch you. . . ."

At her whispered request his eyes gleamed darkly with amusement and delight. Forcing herself out of the pleasure-induced haze, she trailed her hands down his body and touched him with exquisite care. His breath rasped in his throat. Encouraged, she grew bolder. For a long, heady length of time she learned the contours of him until at last he shuddered under her hands . . . and moved over her. Her body eager and receptive, she gave herself to him, feeling, with a sense of sheer joy, the exploding sensation of delight that followed. This was what her body had been created for, this was what she had been waiting all her life to feel. She reached up to touch his face. "Devlin—"

"Yes," he whispered, as if he knew exactly what she wanted to say. "Yes."

She had been alone all her life, she had been lacking. Now she was whole. Together with Devlin, she was more, much more than she had ever been in her life, more alive, more real, more in touch with all the elemental joys of living. She would never again be able to look at him without remembering this moment of ultimate joining. Even if she never saw him again, a part of his life would always be hers.

Then his slow, gentle movements became more passionate, and her thoughts slid away and in its place came light bursts of sensation and ecstasy. . . .

Lying beside her, he traced her shoulder bone idly, then let his hand drift downward to brush the underside of her breast. Her flesh was like creamy silk under his hand. He felt sated, good. Very good. And yet . . . at just the touch of her he remembered what they had shared, what they could share again. He had to find a way to bridge the gap between them, to tear down the barriers in her mind. He had to find a way to claim her as his. All those things he had never felt before with a woman he'd made love to, the tenderness, the protectiveness, welled up inside him. He felt the way he had that first night when she had been sick and he'd stayed with her. He had known then that he'd never be satisfied until he'd made love to her. Now he knew he'd never be satisfied at all, that he wanted to go on making love to her the rest of his life. Somehow he had to keep her here without showing her how strongly he felt and frightening her away.

Now it's over, really over. Now I must get dressed and leave him. And I don't want to. Dear God, I don't want to.

"I'll get you a robe," he said with a cool casualness that pierced her heart. He rose gracefully with a male unselfconsciousness and walked across the carpeted expanse to disappear down the hall.

141

Now, her mind whispered. *Now. Leave before he comes back to ask you, in that same cool, polite voice, if you want a drink before you go, or something to eat.* She could stand anything but his casual politeness.

Her hands shook as she pulled on her lace bikinis and pushed her legs into the jump suit. She stood up and hunched her shoulders into it, trying to button the buttons, but in her haste her fingers were clumsy and uncooperative. She thrust her feet in her sandals and ran to the closet next to the door. She was pulling her jacket from it and collecting her purse when he appeared across the room.

"What the hell . . ."

In a few quick strides he was beside her. Just as she was reaching up to pull the safety chain away from the door, he grasped her arm and jerked her around. "What were you going to do—" he muttered, his eyes blazing, "walk out of here without saying a damn word?"

Stiff with pride, she faced him, her chin high. "There's really nothing more to say, is there?"

"There's a hell of a lot more to say, and you know it."

The silky gray garment he had meant for her dangled from the crook of his arm. He wore a royal-blue terry robe that came just to his knees and she was forced to fight off the potent male attraction of him and the memory of what they had so recently shared. She said, "What's the matter?" in a cool, remote voice that sounded nothing like her own. "Haven't I completed the prescribed set of activities? Was I supposed to stay for a drink? Or do you always serve breakfast to your overnight guests?"

His jaw clenched. She had struck a nerve, but he was holding on to his temper with a determination evident in the hard planes of his face, the tightening of his grip on her arm. "You can't walk out on me," he growled, "I'm not ready to let you go," and knew the moment the words were out of his mouth he had said the worst possible thing to her.

142

Her cheeks flaming, her eyes brilliant, she said, "I stay or go as I please. No man tells me what to do."

He was exasperated, but he contained his irritation and said in a more modulated tone, "That's not what I meant. Carolyn, listen to me. We both know it can't end like this. Stay with me"—desperately he searched for something, some bargaining point—"at least until it's light." He thought at a frantic pace, remembered what she'd said about his pilot. She'd been worried about his disturbed night. "I'll call Bob and tell him to get some sleep and we'll have breakfast and do the same."

Amazingly her stomach made a rumbling sound as if the mere mention of food had set off a reaction. He heard it, and smiled down at her, a melting male smile that weakened her resolve. "Are you always hungry afterward?"

She examined his face for a trace of mockery and found none. "The occasion hasn't arisen enough for me to know," she said frankly.

"Thank God for that." His voice had a fervent quality that shocked her. It was almost as if he really cared. Then he said, "It's no wonder your stomach is complaining. It's four o'clock in the morning and you've had nothing to eat for hours. Let me fix you something." His grip shifted, and with almost no movement at all he guided her back into the living room. He tossed the gray robe on the couch as they passed it, and she found herself being led up the stairs into the dinette, her traitorous body letting his light but firm grip on her arm carry her along.

He guided her through a swinging door into a large and luxurious kitchen. The walls were paneled halfway up with a rich cedar-colored wood, and above a dark oak chair rail the wallpaper was brown and glossy. It reminded her of his eyes. Hanging copper pans and a round table tucked into the corner gave the room an old-fashioned warmth combined with streamlined efficiency.

"Omelet or scrambled?"

"Whichever you prefer."

143

He reached for the omelet pan, aware of the slow, heavy throb of his heart in his chest. He had almost lost her. Another moment and she would have walked out the door. Right now she was hovering in the doorway as if any minute she would bolt. "Sit down," he said, gesturing with his head toward the comfortable swivel chairs around the table.

He wasn't watching her overtly, but he could feel her hesitation. He went on with his preparations, taking the eggs from the refrigerator, cracking them into a bowl, whipping them into a golden froth.

At last she crossed the room behind him and seated herself in one of the chairs, turning it slightly so she was facing him. He relaxed a little, but she was still so wary that she reminded him of a boxer who was afraid to let his opponent walk behind him. She didn't trust him. There was no reason that she should. They were enemies in every respect except one. . . .

He had already proven she was susceptible to him. He had made love to her. But what had he gained by it? He wanted more than physical possession. He wanted a hold on her emotions. How could he break down the wall around her heart? Her stubborn pride and her experience with Jed had made her independent and wary. Yet it was that very independence, that spirit, that had attracted him in the first place. He wanted her exactly the way she was, without a single change. How rare that was! The other women who had captured his interest enough to make their way into his life had all annoyed him in small ways—or very large ones. Most of his irritation had stemmed from their possessiveness. Carolyn, on the other hand, was as elusive as a summer breeze. He had possessed her—but it had been a brief possession only.

She said dryly, "Do you always whip the eggs as if you were going to beat them to death?"

She sat waiting, knowing she had said what she did because she couldn't stand his silent detachment any longer. He raised dark eyes to her, their brown depths glazed over. He had been deep in thought about something that had nothing to do with her. They had just shared the most intimate act a man and a woman could share, and now, he seemed to have forgotten her existence.

"I was—thinking about something," he said, and handily poured the yellow liquid into the pan.

She forced herself to a coolness that she was far from feeling, but one that matched his own. "A corporate problem."

"You might say that."

"We still haven't come to an agreement."

He adjusted the heat on the burner, turned his back to the stove, and faced her, leaning against the counter, his arms folded across his chest. "What do you want me to do?"

"You know what I want you to do," she said, her tone flat. "I can't sell you my stock."

"Why?"

"I have too much invested. The only way for me to show a profit now is to keep on buying and gain control."

The sick feeling in the pit of her stomach threatened to overwhelm her. "I should have known you wouldn't change your mind."

"Yes," he said softly, his eyes impaling her, his avid interest in the contours of her face making up for his lack of attention a moment ago, "you should have." He let the silence build and then he said softly, "Did you think that if you let me make love to you I would have a change of heart?"

She lifted her chin, fury welling through her like a flash fire. "That would be a little difficult, wouldn't it, since you don't have a heart!"

"I'm beginning to think yours is wrapped with ticker tape," he murmured. "A direct line to the stock market."

She shot up out of the chair, but in the two steps she managed to take toward the door, he was on her, catching her arm and swinging her around.

"That's your solution to everything, isn't it?" he said smoothly, the hard grip of his fingers on her upper arm the only sign of his temper. "Attack and run."

She glared at him, her temper flashing from blue eyes gone wide and smoky with anger. "Let go of me." The slight sulfur smell of overcooked eggs drifted to her nose. "Your omelet is burning."

"Let the damn thing burn." He stared back at her with a hard determination, his hold not loosening an inch. "Listen to me, honey, and listen well. I'm going to take over your company, and when I do . . . you'll be working for me. If you quit—or even try to run away—I'll fire every employee of yours within twenty-four hours and replace them within a week. Do you understand?"

CHAPTER EIGHT

It was a bluff, and he knew it, but he had too much at stake not to try anything that would make her realize she had to stop fighting him.

"You wouldn't—do that." The words were breathless, testing.

"You think not?"

His face was sculptured stone. "Yes," she murmured, "you would, wouldn't you? You wouldn't hesitate to use other people to your own advantage."

For a moment he stared at her in the electric silence. Then his mouth softened and his eyes moved lazily over her. "It can't be advantageous for both sides. Your employees have a job . . . and you have me."

"I don't want you," she cried.

He caught her arm. "You're lying, honey—to me and to yourself. You're here right now because you can't stay away from me any more than I can stay away from you."

She shook her arm, trying to loosen his grip. "Take your hands off me and I'll show you how far away I can stay from you."

He was angry, and his fingers tightened on her wrist, drawing her closer. "You accepted my invitation with very little persuasion and you came—wearing a provocative suit and damn little underneath it. Is that the normal behavior of a woman who doesn't want a man?"

"I didn't intend—"

"Didn't you?" he cut in sharply. "I think you did. I think you enjoyed the thought that you were putting another woman out of my bed."

She lifted her head, her eyes wide with pride and pain. "I couldn't care less—"

"Oh, you care, all right," he murmured, pulling her close. "You just can't let yourself admit how much—"

He slid the fingers of his free hand around her throat, trapping her with a clamping hold that still managed to be gentle. Those masculine fingertips provoked a thousand tiny sensual memories that made her body tremble. His mouth settled on hers with the ease and familiarity of a lover while one hand reached behind her. She heard the soft click of the switch for the burner and knew he had turned off the omelet. "Devlin, no —"

"Yes, Carolyn."

He kissed her again, his lips coaxing and teasing and moistening her own, his tongue cajoling and probing and testing her resistance until there was no resistance left to test. He picked her up and carried her out of the kitchen and down the hall to the bedroom. One lamp was lit by the bed, the lamp that had been on when he talked to her on the phone, perhaps. The bed was made, the covers all neatly tucked under. He stood there with her in his arms, arrogantly masculine and sure of himself, holding her tall body easily, watching the path her eyes took. His soft laugh was like an aphrodisiac, an almost physical touch as his warm breath caressed her face. "Do you believe me now?"

He laid her down. Released from his arms, she recovered a measure of sanity. She began to rise from the bed, trying to get up, but he caught her and trapped her against the pillow, his steel fingers pressing down on her shoulders. She fought the battle against his attraction and her own weakening to her aching need for him. Her body was nothing but a repository of leaping nerves under those hard hands and those eyes that examined her so ruthlessly. He looked into her soul and saw the battle raging. His mouth curved with amusement as he lowered his head. She clamped her lips together, but her mouth was not his destination. He bent lower to trail little bites alternately with kisses along the sensitive curve of her throat, nipping and caressing in a dazzling array of sensual expertise, sending her off on another reeling round of tingling anticipation. A hand left her shoulder, and in another instant the buttons of her jump suit were unfastened, and his fingers and mouth were exploring those warm curves with a slow gentleness that gave rise to a passion in her loins that was anything but gentle. When he pushed the material aside and his mouth found an exquisite center, she was devastated and exalted. He made her his slave—yet she was his captor, too, for as her breathing grew more shallow, and her hands moved lower on his body, his own breath rasped in his throat. Wordlessly she stared up at him, her eyes wide and pleading.

He drew away, shed his robe, and came back to her, naked, gloriously male, more real than anything she had ever seen in her life, muscle and bone moving smoothly under bronzed skin as he lay down beside her and propped his head up on one elbow to look into her face.

"Do you believe in role reversal, honey?" he whispered, bending closer yet supporting himself so that she felt nothing but the light kisses he was brushing on her cheek, her mouth, her nose.

"I don't know," she murmured, confused.

He raised her hand and touched it to his lips, kissing it. Then, with a slow provocative movement of his tongue, he washed the center of her palm, making her aware of a network of nerves she hadn't known she possessed, running from her hand to the center of her body.

"I've taken off my clothes first," he murmured. "I've made myself totally vulnerable to you. If you want to walk away from me"—his eyes were fastened on hers as if they would never leave her—"I can't stop you." He eased himself away from her, waiting. He thought he had never been more aware of a woman. Her hair was attractively tousled around her head, dark strands of satin against the white pillow, her cheeks were flushed, her eyes

149

dark and dilated with sexual arousal, and the siren beauty of her bare curves peeked from between the edges of the jump suit, their nipples tautly pressing against the nubby cloth. He wanted her with a strength and a passion that surprised him. He was taking a risk, he knew, a calculated risk. But he was no longer satisfied to seduce her, arouse her, take her. He had to show her that her needs, her emotions, her woman's body was as involved with him as he was with her. . . .

She thought about it. She thought about getting up and walking away, watching his face as she did it. She rolled to one side and got off the bed, not really sure what she was going to do, knowing only that she needed to move away from him in order to think more clearly. She turned around and in the circle of light where he lay like a Greek statue of masculine beauty, a flicker of pain darkened his eyes, and she knew that it was a mere shadow of what she would feel if she walked away. Antagonism, anger, pride, slid into nothingness. Nothing was left but the overriding feeling that belonging to Devlin once more was worth any pain in the aftermath. Slowly her hands went to the shoulders of her jump suit. She drew it down, slowly, provocatively. He watched, and as he did, the pain in his eyes disappeared, and in its place a smoky desire flared. His mouth lifted slightly at the corners, his passion held in iron-tight control, his body the only betraying sign of his arousal. As her pale slenderness emerged just beyond the circle of the lamplight, his gaze seemed to warm the very coolness of her skin. When she lay down beside him, his restraint shattered and he grasped her and pulled her roughly to him. She gloried in his urgency, and with her mouth and hands she told him she was ready. He lifted her and settled her body over his, his thighs nudging erotically between hers, his hard male body thrusting into her softness. Her passion soared and seared him with a hunger as explosive as his own.

She woke to a room filled with morning light and Devlin's

voice talking softly on the phone. "Take all my calls, and come and get the material you'll need to represent me at the meeting today."

"Devlin," she said sleepily, her hand going out to touch a bare, muscular arm. He cradled the phone. "Good morning." He kissed her, his lips taking hers in a tender, slow kiss, his bare body covering hers possessively.

"Devlin, you said you had a meeting at nine o'clock."

"Milt's covering for me."

"I—don't want you to rearrange your schedule for me."

"You don't?" His hand traced lazily down under the sheet over the top of her hipbone and down her smooth thigh.

His questing fingertips found what they sought and she clutched his shoulders as tiny shivers of delight prickled over her skin. "Maybe you could go later," she whispered, forcing the words out past a throat gone dry.

"Yes," he muttered. "I could go later."

A day and a half later, in the afternoon, the phone rang. "Are you coming up for air soon?" Milt asked dryly.

Holding the receiver, Devlin rolled over in bed to look at the woman sitting cross-legged beside him. His naked skin gleaming, his mouth widened in a lazy smile, he took in the tousled dark-ness of her hair, the rosy gleam of her skin. Her bare knees poking out from under the tails of his shirt, she plucked a grape off the cluster she held and popped it into her mouth. She was wearing his blue shirt, the sleeves rolled up, the top of it comfort-ably unbuttoned halfway, exposing the tops of her full breasts.

Into the phone Devlin said, "Problems?"

"Nothing pressing—except the abusive language I've been getting from Miss Lawrence."

"What seems to be the problem?"

"She doesn't understand why all your calls are being routed to me. She doesn't like talking to me. She wants to talk to you."

"Too bad. Keep on with the present course of action."

151

"Yeah, sure," Milt said dryly. "Carolyn is there with you now, I take it."

"You always did have the ability to analyze a situation quickly and well. Anything else?"

"Seattle's making noises again. And there's a rumored gold-strike in Nevada close to that property you bought last month." Milt hesitated, then drawled, "When you're through staking a claim here, you should get out there and do the same."

His mouth twisted in a wry grin. "I'll have to check that out. Anything else?"

"Yeah. Can you give me a rough estimate on your expected time of arrival back to the real world?"

He looked up at Carolyn, his gaze taking in the creamy, delectable line of her throat as she lifted her head. "Another twenty-four hours, I should think."

When he cradled the phone, she looked at him, her eyes curiously amused. "Pressing business?"

"Nothing that Milt can't handle," he said, catching her shoulders and bending his head to nuzzle the throat that had been tantalizing him with its smooth gleam.

"Aren't you hungry?" She plucked a tiny piece of the fruit from the cluster and wedged it between her skin and his lips.

"Yes." He accepted the morsel from her fingers, ate it, and then, as if the grape had affected him, he gave her a comic leer, his fingers traveling idly down the front of the shirt she wore to trace the outer edges of the rounded curve exposed to his gaze. "I'm still hungry."

She laughed up at him, her eyes sparkling with a self-confidence that had not been there a day ago. She felt warmed, loved, assured in her womanhood as she had never been before in her life. They had slept, cooked another omelet and managed not to burn it, made love, slept, and she had just returned from the kitchen with cheeses, crackers, and grapes when the phone had rung. "You have an insatiable appetite, Mr. Halliday," she told him, pushing back a dark strand of hair from the top of his right ear, and then tracing over the shell lightly with the tip of her fingernail.

With one smooth move he pulled her feet straight in front of her and leaned over her, pushing aside the blue cotton and taking the center of her already hardening bud into his mouth. Against her skin he murmured, "And you, Miss Wakefield, have the infinite capacity to satisfy. You are my appetizer"—his tongue circled slowly round the dusky peak, sending delicious little tingles of anticipation curling through her—"and my entrée"—his hand wandered lower, discovered the sensitive core of her—"and my dessert."

She stood in the kitchen with him, watching him take the steaks from the refrigerator and prepare them for the grill. In his silvery gray robe, bracing herself against the counter, she felt a light freedom, a wonderful awareness of every inch of her body that she had never felt before. She was vulnerable, yet protected, free to soar, yet tied forever to this man who moved around with the lithe ease of an athlete. She shouldn't be feeling this way. She shouldn't be so happy. It was all a dream, and any minute the bubble would burst.

"How do you want your steak?"

"With you," she murmured.

He glanced up, a smile crinkling his eyes, curving his lips. His skin looked smooth and dark against the blue terry-cloth robe he wore. "That goes without saying. How do you want it cooked?"

"Medium."

"Good. I hate having to charbroil the life out of a good cut of beef."

The bubble of her happiness burst with one quick pop. "Like you usually have to do for your women?"

The smile faded. He dropped the steak from the end of the long-handled fork onto the flat surface, his face dark.

"I'm sorry," she said at once. "I—maybe I'm just trying to keep things in perspective."

"Your 'perspective' is cockeyed."

"Is it?"

"I've asked you to live with me."

She shook her head, her eyes on the floor. "You know I can't do that."

He hesitated. A cool look of unconcern wiped the emotion from his face. "I've also asked you to marry me."

She lifted her head, the taut line of her throat at a proud angle. "And how long would our marriage last? Until the next attractive woman walked into your life and threw herself at you?"

He stared at her and then turned toward the grill, picking up the fork and flipping the steaks over carefully, controlled anger in every movement of his body. "Stop being so damned insecure."

"It isn't a matter of insecurity, it's a matter of reality."

He laid the fork down and turned toward her slowly, folding his hands and putting them over his chest. "Your reality? Or mine?"

She didn't answer.

"I try to be patient with you," he said huskily. "I try to remember you were raised in—awkward circumstances. But at some point in time we all have to grow up and accept the responsibility for what we are."

She whispered, "What do you want me to do?"

He stared at her. "I want you to trust me."

She shook her head. "I'm afraid. Not because of you. Because of me. I don't deserve such a wonderful thing to happen to me. . . ."

In one swift step he came to her. "You deserve," he said softly, catching her into his arms and pulling her close, "all the good things life has to give."

Through her tears she smiled up at him. "There's one thing I don't think I'm going to get."

"What's that?" His mouth closed in on hers.

"A medium steak. I think it just passed the well-done stage."

He kissed her, a quick hard kiss, and turned back to the grill to grab up the fork and rescue the burning meat. "I give up," he groaned. "Trying to cook with you in my kitchen is impossible."

"That's okay," she said, slipping her arms around his waist from behind and pressing her body against his, loving the feel of the hard muscle and bone of his back against the softness of her breasts. "They'll taste just fine."

They scraped the charcoal off the steaks and ate their meal in the living room seated on the floor around the low table. When they'd finished, they drank wine, and then they made love— slow, long, luxurious love. She savored every moment of it, but afterward, when she lay in his arms, he seemed restless, distracted, and she knew the time had come for her to leave. Without a word she rose and went into the bedroom and began to dress.

When she came out, he was wearing the terry robe and sitting in a corner of the couch, a brooding look on his face.

"Will you call your pilot?" She smiled. "He should be rested by now."

"I don't want you to go."

"I must. Tomorrow is Monday, and I have to go to work . . . and so do you."

He pushed himself up and disappeared into the bedroom. When he came out, he was dressed in jeans and a cream tan knit shirt. "I'll walk down to the lobby with you."

"There's no need—"

His mouth tightened. "I need," he said succinctly, and she closed her mouth and nodded, her heart pounding in reaction to the intensity in his voice.

Inside the elevator he was quiet, his head lifted as he watched the numbers flashing. When the door opened, his hand on her elbow was possessive.

At six o'clock in the evening the lobby was bustling with life.

155

A man and woman, each carrying a suitcase, stood at the desk waiting to check in. Another group of men and women stood laughing and talking just at the bottom of the steps that led to the dining room. And in the middle of the room, surrounded by three large suitcases, sat a young blond woman. She wore a bored look on her face and an electric-blue suit that was fitted with micrometric precision to the voluptuous curves of her body. Her eyes traveled to Devlin, and she moved then, languidly stretching and getting to her feet.

"Hello, Devlin."

The throaty voice was as recognizable as the slimly curved body. Carolyn made a slight move as if to step away from Devlin, but his grip on her elbow tightened.

"Hello, Kristin. What are you doing in Chicago?"

"Waiting to see you, obviously." The actress's green eyes flickered over Carolyn. "Milt said you were busy."

"I am. You should have phoned first and saved yourself the trip."

"I did call." There was a cold, calculating anger in the green depths. "I guess I just wanted to check things out myself."

"If you'll excuse me," Carolyn murmured, but there was no escaping that unrelenting grip on her arm unless she wanted to make a bigger scene than the one already in progress. They were drawing some attention, Kristin's flamboyant costume and model-perfect looks attracting the stares of both men and women. Carolyn tugged at her arm, but Devlin merely drew her closer.

"You've made a trip for nothing, Kris," he said coolly.

"So I see," the young woman drawled, her eyes going pointedly to Carolyn. There was a long, awkward silence. Kristin Lawrence stared at Devlin, and then at Carolyn, as if assessing her chances. Then, under the electric-blue suit jacket, an elegant shoulder moved. "Well, that's the breaks. You win a few, lose a few."

She went back to her luggage, pride making her back ramrod straight. She raised a hand and made an eloquent gesture to a red-jacketed bell captain. He hastened to her side immediately. "I'll need someone to help me get these into a taxi."

Devlin turned to Carolyn, his face bleak, his eyes narrowed with pain. "I suppose this only confirms what you wanted to believe."

To his utter astonishment she stood on tiptoe, put a light hand on his arm, and leaned forward to press her mouth on his. Too stunned to react fully to her kiss, he merely accepted it.

She tilted her head away and smiled up at him, and he thought he had never seen such a beautiful sight. "If you could see your face," she whispered.

"Can you see it?" He clasped her cheeks between his palms, gazing down into her eyes with an avid attention that brought smiles to the faces of those people who were still watching them. "Can you see the truth?"

She laughed, a low, amused chuckle. "Devlin, you look like a thundercloud. Stop scowling."

He stared at her, his eyes brilliant, his face rawly expressive. "I love you." The unwillingness in his tone, the forced and throaty sound of those beautiful words, convinced her as no outcry of passion ever could.

She braced herself against his hard body and reached up to kiss his cheek. Before he could react, she slipped out from under his slackened grip. "I'm glad you waited until we were in a crowded hotel lobby to tell me that," she said huskily, "or I wouldn't have the strength to leave you."

"Then, don't," he rasped, but she pivoted out of his reach and ran down the steps. He saw her pull open the glass door and climb into the waiting car, his car, the car that was taking her away from him.

"Have some dessert, Carolyn," Jed ordered her as she sat in the dark and elegant dining room two nights after her return. She flushed, and aware of her rosy skin and the way his eyes were

157

playing over her red cheeks, she shook her head. "No, thanks, I couldn't eat another thing. It was all—delicious."

She colored even more deeply. Jed helped himself to a generous serving of the pecan pie he wasn't supposed to have and said with uncanny perception, "So you went to Chicago to see Halliday." Jed sat back, his legs stretched under the table, his eyes traveling over her face with a keen, assessing gaze. She strove for a smooth, unexpressive face and sipped her coffee.

"Yes."

"Get him to sell his stock?" Jed finished his pie and started on his brandy. The apricot and the fruity smell teased her nose. "No."

"Too bad." He took a sip, closed his eyes in appreciation. "Now what?"

"I don't know. I have nothing left to go on."

"Are you asking me for help?"

She shook her head. "No. I don't think even you could help me now."

From over the top of the brandy glass Jed gazed at her shrewdly. "Are you in love with him?"

"Yes."

"Did he ask you to marry him?"

"Yes."

Jed's face broke into a broad smile. "When's the wedding?"

"There isn't going to be a wedding, Jed."

The glass came down on the table with a force that had Carolyn worrying about the state of the fragile crystal. "What do you mean there isn't going to be a wedding?"

She met his eyes over the candlelit linen, the elegant table service. "Were you counting on a wedding, Jed?"

His face suffused with color. "That's the logical progression of events when two people—"

"It wasn't for my mother, was it?"

He gave a slow, heavy sigh. "You've never forgiven me for that, have you?" His hand shook slightly as he reached for the

158

glass again and lifted it to his lips. "Neither has Donna. Neither one of you can forgive or forget." He drank and then set the glass on the table. "I didn't know she was expecting you, you know."

"What difference would it have made?"

"It would have made a difference. I might have—had the courage to face Elizabeth and tell her the truth." He lifted his head. "Devlin doesn't have a wife. There's no reason you can't be married—"

"Maybe Devlin doesn't want to marry me," she said, skirting the truth.

"But I told him—" He stopped suddenly and his mouth clamped shut, and something about his sudden catching back of the words alerted Carolyn. She snapped to attention, every sense alert. "What did you tell him, Jed?"

He shook his head and stared at her, a stricken look lurking in his blue eyes.

"Knowing you as I do," she said softly, watching him, "I'd take a guess and say that you left nothing to chance." She paused, her stomach aching, her mind recoiling from the thoughts that poured in. "What did you offer him in return for a marriage proposal, Jed? A promise not to bail me out? Stock in your own company?" She lifted her head and tears glittered in those blue eyes so like his. "What exactly am I worth on the stock exchange, Jed?"

CHAPTER NINE

"Dammit, Carolyn—"

She felt betrayed. Jed's stock offer made a mockery of every moment she had spent with Devlin. "No, damn *you*, Jed," she said fiercely. "Damn you for interfering in my life."

He stood up and flattened his palms on the table and roared, "Do you think I wanted what happened to your mother to happen to you?"

Too angry to care what she said, she shot back, "I wouldn't think you'd give a damn."

From across the table his eyes burned into hers like the eyes of a tiger cornered in a cage. "I give a damn."

"Stay out of my life," she cried. "Let me make my own mistakes."

Jed stared at her for a long, poignant moment. Then he slumped and sat back down heavily in the chair. "Halliday has refused my offer, then."

"He didn't refuse. He asked me to marry him. I told him no."

"Why, for God's sake? You love him. And he loves you." There was a pleading, almost desperate quality in Jed's voice that was totally foreign to it. Something about it goaded her to reply, "You say that very glibly, Jed. What do you know of love?"

He raised his head and stared at her, his blue eyes alive with an inner fire that seemed to burn his skin. "A damn sight more than you do. I've lived without it for thirty years, young lady, and let me tell you that teaches you something about love." He swallowed and then said in a harsh, grating tone, "I loved your mother—and I love you. And nothing you say or do will ever change that." He took a breath and then went on. "And if you love Halliday, you'd better reach out with both hands and grab him. Love is too damn precious to throw away." Then, with a dignity that made her throat ache, he got up from the chair and walked out of the room.

He was nowhere in sight when she walked into the cavernous lounge, and after a moment's hesitation, she collected her purse and let herself out the door. She couldn't talk to him. Her emotions were too volatile to be trusted. Ever since she had come to live with Jed twelve years ago, they had achieved a sort of armed truce. After their first confrontation, they had carefully skirted the topic of her mother. Now it had all come out in the open, the anger, the hurt, the bitter resentment and regret. She drove automatically, her eyes seeing Jed's face rather than the street. He had suffered just as her mother had suffered. Perhaps Elizabeth had suffered, too, and that made Donna unhappy. But Carolyn's mother was dead and Jed's wife, Elizabeth, was dead. Only she and Jed were left. And somehow they had to find a way to live without tearing each other apart. And they had to find a way to stop the past from destroying the future. Was it already too late? Because of what had happened thirty-one years ago, Jed had bribed Devlin to offer her marriage. But had Devlin accepted the offer? Jed didn't seem certain that he had. And she wasn't sure she could bear to learn the truth.

She parked the car and got out into the cool night air, a light breeze fanning her heated face. She opened the outer door with her key and walked up the stairs. Anger pulsed through her body as she let herself into the apartment. No wonder Devlin had been so ardent, so adamant about getting a commitment from her. He was a company raider, driven by the need to acquire, and if she knew Jed, which she did, he had dangled exactly the right bait, a large block of stock in his own company, probably.

And Devlin had dangled exactly the right bait for her, a husky declaration of love in full view of half the people in the Plaza Hotel. It hadn't seemed calculated—which made it all the more insidious. A grim little smile played over her lips as she went into the bathroom. It was ironic, really. It had been Kristin Lawrence's reaction that had convinced her of Devlin's sincerity. Kristin had taken her time and looked the two of them over coolly. It was Devlin's face that had arrested most of the actress's attention, and it had been Devlin's face that sent her away shrugging, lifting a languid hand for help with her luggage. Carolyn's eyes were blinded by love. Kristin's obviously weren't, but what she had seen in Devlin's face had sent her spinning away to return to her own orbit. Had the actress been fooled just as she had? She remembered Devlin sitting at the oak table in her office, his face cool and contained, not a clue to his emotions surfacing in those brown eyes. As a university professor he had had a marvelous ability to read poetry and inject life into the printed page. It was entirely possible he was a consummate actor. The thought was not a pleasant one.

The next evening, just as she was ready to go into the bathroom for her shower, the phone rang. She stared at it, listening to the strident bell give its urgent summons. On the fourth ring, like a swimmer in deep water, she moved toward it.

"Hello?"

"Well, hello," Devlin said, the deep warmth in his voice sending a chill crawling up her spine. "I was almost ready to give up."

"That doesn't sound like you."

Silence echoed back across the wire. Even in those brief words he had caught the hint of hostility.

"Hard day at the office?"

"Nothing more than usual."

In the silence that followed, she could almost feel him assessing her words, assaying them for the nugget of truth. His voice a shade cooler, he said, "I'll be flying out to Nevada for a few days. I want you to come and spend the weekend with me."

She waited, turning her head away from the receiver so he

162

couldn't hear her quickened breathing. When she had more control, she composed her excuse. "I'm sorry. I've made other plans."

"I see." His voice was as polite as her own. "I'm not sure what my schedule will be until I get out there and find out what's going on. Are you staying in town? I'll call you."

Caught, she hesitated, then decided a bigger lie was as good as a small one. "No."

She had driven him over the edge with that. "Carolyn, I thought we had things settled. What's happened?"

"I don't know what you mean."

"You damn well do." He was angry now, and the frustrated temper was just barely held in control. He sounded as though he wanted to come through the phone at her. The thought pleased her. Let him be frustrated. Let him feel just a small measure of the anguish it was causing her to hear his voice and know she would never again lie in his arms, never again hear those husky words of love murmured against her skin. "What's happened?"

"Reason happened. Sanity happened."

He cursed softly. "I knew I never should have let you walk away from me Sunday night."

"Yes," she taunted softly. "Your prize got away, didn't it?"

"Prize? Dammit, what are you talking about?"

"I'm talking about playing to win, Mr. Halliday. That's what you always do, isn't it?" She fired the words at him with a low intensity that made her voice tremble.

A long silence was her only answer. Then, as coolly contained as if they were discussing the weather, he said, "You've been talking to Jed."

"Yes."

"And you've tried and convicted me without even bothering to listen to my side of the story."

"Did you discuss me with Jed?"

"Yes," came the soft answer.

"He offered you stock?"

163

"Yes," he said again, sounding more frustrated, "but—"

"And you took it."

"I took nothing! Dammit, Carolyn, I can't talk to you about this over the phone. I've got to see you. I'll send Bob to pick you up on Saturday. . . ."

"I won't be here."

"You'd better be."

"Don't count on it, Mr. Halliday." She lowered the receiver and cradled it softly. It rang before she got to the bathroom door. She ignored it and got undressed to take her shower.

In the week that followed her phone rang with monotonous regularity through the evening. She learned to ignore it, and finally resorted to a trick she had learned to block the warning buzz that sounded if she took the phone off the hook. On a night during the second endless week since she had spoken with Devlin, she was watching television when her doorbell rang.

It was Jed, with fire in his eye. "Why the hell aren't you answering your phone?"

"I haven't wanted to," she said, staring straight at him.

He ran a hand through his thick hair and cast a look around the hall. "Aren't you going to ask me in?"

"Yes, of course." She stepped back to allow him access to the apartment, but if he said one word about Devlin Halliday, she'd have to restrain herself from throwing him forcibly out again. Something of her thoughts must have penetrated, because he was eyeing her warily. "I got a call from a woman named Mrs. Carlson. Wanted me to check and see if you were all right. She's been trying to contact you to tell you her son is in the hospital."

The lethargy she had shrouded herself in fell away. "What happened? What's wrong? Did she say?"

"Seems he broke his leg playing soccer." Jed gave her a curious look. "Seems he wants you to come and see him. Said something about having to cancel a fishing trip he had planned with you."

"Yes, we were going out this Saturday."

"I'll take you to the hospital if you want me to."

"That's not necessary. I can drive myself and you won't have to wait around for me."

He gave a heavy sigh. "Are you shutting us both out of your life?"

She didn't have to ask who he meant by "us." "Jed," she said softly. "I need time."

"I never intended to hurt you." He reached for her, a strange, groping gesture that was totally unlike him. "I only wanted the best for you."

Like any father, she thought humbly, and made a move toward him. With poignant appeal in every line of his face, he opened his arms. She walked into them and nestled against him. "I should be going to the hospital," she said huskily.

"You should be having your own kids instead of playing nursemaid to someone else's," he muttered in her ear.

In spite of herself she pulled away from him and laughed up into his face. "Oh, Jed, you're impossible. You have a one-track mind, do you know that? You'd do anything to have those grandchildren, wouldn't you?"

He drew back, his face startled. "Certainly not. I wouldn't want you to take up with some stupid fool who would father children as stupid as he was."

She shook her head, caught up in a helpless spasm of mirth that teetered on the brink of tears. "I'll try not to marry anyone stupid."

He gave her a funny little look, one she would have been suspicious of, if she hadn't been distracted by her thoughts about Keith. She stepped away and gave him a little push. "Go on home. I'll call you when I get back from the hospital."

Twenty minutes later she walked into the hospital room where Keith Carlson lay with his leg in traction and the smell of antiseptic and fresh plaster cast assailed her nose. Keith looked fretfully uncomfortable. He cast a rueful eye over her, and then up at his encased leg cradled by a sling affair that hung from the ceiling. "Think I'll be out of this by skiing season?"

Feeling an instant sympathy for him, she said, "I don't know," and went to the side of the bed to slip her hand in his. Keith had always been so active. He would find it hard to tolerate confinement in a cast. "What do the doctors say?"

"They won't promise anything definite. Depends on my veins, or something."

"Well, your veins are young," she reassured him.

He made a face. "Right now they feel about a hundred years old. I'm sorry about our fishing trip."

"Don't worry. There'll be plenty of fish left in the river for another time."

"Mom said you were having trouble with your phone or something."

"Something," she agreed noncommittally, leaning her hip against the edge of the bed. Keith had not let go of her hand.

"How are things at the plant?"

"Slow. We're just doing repair on a couple of old models right now. Mostly everyone's waiting for the change in command."

"You're really letting him have the place, then?" he asked, a tinge of regret in his tone.

She had told Keith about Halliday's imminent takeover; in a town the size of LaCrosse it was hardly a secret.

She tried a slight smile. "It's not a matter of *letting* him have it. He's already bought a controlling interest of the shares. Now all he needs is the go ahead from the Securities and Exchange Commission. The stockholders' meeting in the spring will be just a formality."

"My cousin works there. Rumor has it everyone's guaranteed their job for three years."

She nodded. "That's right."

He squinted at her, made a restless movement, and winced. "Isn't that unusual?"

166

"Yes, it is. Most takeovers are followed by a change in personnel rather quickly."

His fingers tightened on hers. "Are you—staying on?"

She heard the wariness in his voice, the attempt to cover up his personal interest in her answer. "Yes." She couldn't tell him she had no choice. Devlin had inserted a clause qualifying the employment guarantee to the continued cooperation and employment of top management. He'd returned the signed papers by mail. She didn't want to see him or talk to him.

"Isn't that going to be a little hard for you? I mean, taking orders from someone else when you're used to being the boss."

Did he remember Devlin Halliday's cool assurance, his self-possession from that one brief glimpse? Evidently he did. She kept her face expressionless and said, "I don't imagine Mr. Halliday will be spending much time in LaCrosse. Leisure Days is too small a company to require his personal attention."

Keith kept his eyes on her face. "Isn't he that guy you were with the night in the park?"

"We weren't together but—yes, that was him."

He let go of her hand and she took a step away from the bed and concentrated on keeping any trace of revealing expression out of her face. "I got—funny vibes from him."

"Did you?" What could she say to that? Devlin Halliday was not a subject she cared to discuss. She tried a diversionary tactic. "How's the food here?"

He made a grimace. "I wouldn't know. They haven't let me eat anything yet."

"How did it happen?" She gestured at his leg. He launched into the story, and when he finished a few moments later, she realized with a guilty start that she hadn't been listening. He went on to tell her how his soccer-team buddies were going to take turns coming in to see him, and she eased her conscience by listening to him more carefully, and when he finished and bit back a yawn, she took her cue. "I'm going to go now and let you get some rest."

He looked sulky and regretful and begged her to stay, but she shook her head. "Perhaps I can come and see you tomorrow." On a sudden impulse she leaned over and kissed his cheek. When she straightened away, she saw that his face was flushed. Lightly she touched his hand. "You get some sleep. Your body needs it."

"I don't want you to go."

"I must," she told him and walked to the door.

"That was a touching scene." Devlin Halliday straightened away from the wall, a mocking smile lifting the corners of his mouth. He wore the gray suit in which she had admired him the morning they had conferred in his office, but somehow it didn't seem to fit him as well as it had that day. It was looser. The lines around his mouth had deepened, too, as if he had lost weight. There was a tiredness in his eyes that matched his aura of strained control.

Shocked by the fact of his presence and his tense look, she said nothing. He took advantage of her stunned insensibility and grasped her elbow, dragging her along the corridor.

"Let go of me."

"If you think I've gone without sleep for two days and flown fifteen hundred miles just to get a polite brush-off in the lobby of a hospital, you can think again." He strong-armed her into her own car, and came around to the other side to slide in under the wheel. "Keys," he said, holding out his hand.

"We have nothing to say to each other," she said coolly.

"You may not, but I have a hell of a lot to say to you and I don't intend to say it in a parked car. Now, would you like me to add purse snatching to the long list of my sins, or will you hand me the keys?"

She took the path of least resistance, dug in her purse, and gave them to him.

He started the engine and drove with unerring accuracy and barely contained temper up the street toward her apartment. When he reached the top and parked the car, she got out before he could come around. Aware of his silent fury with every nerve in her body, she led the way up the stairs. At the top she held out her hand. "I'll need the keys to unlock the door."

He pulled them from his pocket, examined them for a moment, and then unerringly picked the correct one and inserted it in the lock. The door swung open and he made a short, ironic gesture with his hand, directing her to walk through. Her body tense, she crossed the threshold, turned toward him, and held out her hand in a silent request for the return of her key ring. Watching her, his face a dark mask of cynical amusement, he slipped the keys in his pocket. Then he studied her avidly, taking in every detail of the brief sleeveless white dress she wore, his eyes moving slowly along the path of red piping that decorated the button-down-the-front closing to her knees. His frankly intimate examination made an inarticulate sound escape her lips, and no longer able to bear his eyes moving over her, she turned away and went to stand in front of the wall of windows. It was nearly four o'clock in the afternoon, and now, as the last days of September approached, the sun slanted over the country landscape, turning the green and russet land into a land of sun and shadow, hill and valley, cut through by a shimmering ribbon of river.

And into that room darkened by the shadows of a dying day, he said a soft, smoky word. "Why?"

She didn't say anything. She couldn't. The pain and anguish of having him so near and yet so far rose in her throat and lodged there like a physical thing.

He was relentless. "You owe me an explanation, at least."

"You know why," she got out at last. "I—won't be bought."

"Who was buying?"

She turned to him then, her arms going round her body to hug herself as if she were in danger of losing all her vital body heat and freezing to death in a room that was warm and comfortable. "Jed," she began, and when he shook his head, she said in a low, husky voice, "No, let me finish. Jed—offered you a—a bargain, didn't he?"

169

"He offered—but I didn't accept."

She shook her head, and tried to tear her eyes away from him. But she couldn't. Her body was hungry for the sight of his lean tall frame, the way his dark hair lay mussed around his head.

"It doesn't matter. Even if you didn't accept, you still had the advantage. You had Jed on your side." She laughed, a short, hard, unamused laugh. "Jed had an unmarketable commodity. I suppose I can't blame him for trying every way he could to marry off his thirty-year-old illegitimate daughter—"

"Stop it!" he thundered, his face as dark as the shadows in the room as he sprang into action, striding across the room and taking her by the upper arms. "Stop punishing yourself for something you had no control over."

"I should never have agreed to come and live with him," she went on in that same cold, emotionless voice that chilled his blood. Even the skin of her upper arms seemed cool and lifeless to his touch. He had to jar her into life somehow. "I told you I loved you. Doesn't that mean anything?"

"You used to read poems well, too. It's all the same thing, isn't it? The ability to pretend emotion where there is none?"

His mouth twisted. "Is that what you told yourself?"

"I told myself any number of things. I told myself it didn't matter. I told myself that what we shared was so good, so right, nothing could change it—"

"Yes," he breathed, pulling her close.

She braced herself, creating space between them. "But no matter how many times I said it—I still didn't believe it."

He reached for her, and this time his will overrode hers. He gathered her close, holding her in a tight but gentle grip. "You must," he said. "You must trust me. Forget the past, Carolyn. Move into the future—with me."

She was still for a moment, savoring his closeness. In an almost inaudible voice, she said, "I—can't."

He released her suddenly, his arms sliding away, leaving her more chilled than ever. "We shared something wonderful," he said in a strained whisper, "something unique. But no love affair can stand still. It's time to go on from where we started and make a commitment to each other—or call it off."

Her head pounded, her brain reeled. She should have been able to think more clearly out of his arms, but all her clamoring senses wanted was to be gathered back into them and held close to that hard male form. But she couldn't make a move toward him. Like a terrible echo of the past, she remembered Terry and how he had begged her to believe in him, and how, against her better judgment, she had—only to overhear a conversation later in which he admitted to a friend that he had made love to her in order to get close to Jed.

"I can't control what I—feel," she whispered, wishing she could. Her body was screaming with need. She wanted him to take her in his arms and make violent, unending love to her.

He stared at her, his thoughts carefully hidden behind that rugged, masculine face. "I'll be at the motel for another hour. If I don't hear from you before then—I'll know what your answer is."

"If I—did—come to you, Jed's offer would always be between us." She had tossed the words out into the darkening shadows of the room at his back, desperately hoping he would say the miracle words that would take away her hurt.

He turned slowly. "If you think that—I won't bother to wait."

In the breath-held silence she felt a violent ripping inside her.

He said, "We don't exist in a vacuum, Carolyn. We never will. This thing with Jed is probably a small preview of what our life will be like together. Even though I don't condone it, a certain amount of public exposure goes with my life-style. Other people will say and do things that will interfere with our lives." He stopped to let his eyes roam over her slender figure. "If you aren't willing to trust me—and yourself—and what we have together, no matter what people say or do, then there's no sense in our beginning." He shook his head, his eyes holding hers. "We'd tear each other apart within a year." He kept his hand

171

on the knob and gazed at her for another long, heartbreaking moment. She blinked to keep the tears from spilling over. When she looked up again . . . he was gone. The sound of the door closing echoed in her ears with an alien loneliness.

She burned to run to the door, to sprint into the hall and catch him. But pride and fear held her back. She ached with want and need, but he had been so cool, almost—detached. If he loved her, really loved her, how could he walk away?

If you loved him, how could you let him walk away?

She didn't even know how he was getting back to the motel. He would call a taxi from the lobby, she supposed. She should have offered to take him back. She should have gone with him. She should have told him she loved him. But how could she when she was afraid to trust his feelings—afraid to grab for happiness? Yet how could she stay here, existing from one day to the next, knowing that she would never lie in his arms again, knowing that if she saw him at all, it would be on the front page of a tabloid with his current woman, an attractive actress or model, by his side. And yet . . .

Her body froze. Her mind reeled on with a hundred different thoughts. She forced her legs to carry her away from the door toward the wall windows. Below, in the twilight, a winding section of the river shone pale gold in the dying sun. Under that surface of gold lay treacherous snags for passing boats, old limbs of trees waiting to catch on propellers, sandbars that had built up with the shifting river flow, parts of houseboats or barges that had broken up and sunk in the sand only to surface in a new surprising place in the current. Infinitely treacherous, laden with snares for the unwary boater, the river was dangerous, enticing . . . but endlessly fascinating. Its depths contained secrets, and made life interesting for those who traversed its waters. It took skill, audacity, and daring to be a Mississippi River boatman. He had to be aggressive about searching out sandbars and snags, he didn't wait for them to come and find him.

Her life with Devlin would be like that, full of snags. But if

172

she were as aggressive as those hardy river travelers and met hidden traps head on . . .

A sudden surge of joyfulness filled her. She would do something so outrageous, so bold, it would either shock Devlin into refusing or it would remove forever that shadow between them. She whirled around, switching on lights as she dashed across the room. Leaving the living area blazing with light behind her, she half-ran, half-stumbled into her bedroom, kicking off her sensible shoes as she went to her closet. If she was going out, she was going out in style.

Ten minutes later, her hands shaking, she put on her makeup. Her dress, a midnight-blue color, was two-piece, a hem-length buttonless sheer cover-up floating over a strapless tube dress in a silky blue print. High-heeled black patent sandals with gathered straps over her toes enhanced the look of her graceful legs in sheer stockings.

Her breathing quickened as she combed her dark hair with a few jerks of the comb and gathered up her purse. Would Devlin wait that hour he promised to wait? He had to. She would need every moment of it.

The outside coach lamp was lit on Jed's house. She parked the car and ran up the steps. Her impatient stab at the doorbell brought Jed's butler after the second ring.

"Is Jed here?"

"Yes, Miss Wakefield. He's in the drawing room. Come in."

Jed's eyes widened briefly in surprise and she knew that her appearance must have surprised him a great deal for him to betray himself that much. He held a brandy glass in his hand, and instinctively he got to his feet, not out of courtesy, but because he never liked to give anyone the physical advantage of standing over him. "Well, Carolyn. What brings you here tonight?"

"I came to hold you to your word," she said, her voice more husky than she would have liked, her eyes locking on his.

173

"Hold me to my word?" He was genuinely puzzled. He would be even more puzzled in a moment, she was sure.

"How much did you offer Devlin if he agreed to marry me?"

Jed's mouth fell open. Catching himself, he closed it, swallowed. "We didn't discuss a specific amount. . . ."

Her heart soared. Devlin hadn't been lying. "Well, let's discuss a specific amount, Jed."

Jed gaped. "You mean you'll agree?"

"He's offered marriage. I've refused. I'm the one you need to convince. So I'm the one you should buy off. How much, Jed?"

He blinked. "Twenty-five percent of the stock I hold in my company and a place on the board."

She shook her head. "Not enough. Make it thirty and give me the place on your board and we might be talking."

"What!"

"Those are the terms, Jed. Take it or leave it."

His eyes widened, then narrowed. "Do I have your word you'll marry Halliday?"

"Yes."

He stared at her, his face a mixture of incredulity and admiration.

"Well, do we have a deal or not?"

"What the hell is going on?"

"Yes or no, Jed?"

"Yes, dammit," he roared at her.

Coolly, she answered, "Good. I want that stock on my desk the first thing Monday morning." She whirled to go, then turned back. "Oh, and Jed. Endorse the stock to baby Halliday."

Jed's eyebrows flew up. "Baby Halliday?"

"I'll know what the exact name will be in another year. I hope."

Jed's face split into a wide grin.

"Don't get your proud-grandfather look out yet. It isn't a fait accompli. We still have to work on it."

He reached out to pull her close, but she shook her head and evaded his reaching arms. "I don't have time right now for sentimentality. I need written verification of our agreement and I need it immediately."

He stared at her for a long moment, then threw back his head and laughed. He was still chuckling when he went to his desk and scribbled the words on the piece of paper and handed them to her. "My God," he said, laughing up into her face, "it's almost worth all this money to know I've got a daughter like you."

She grinned back at him. "I hope it is," she shot back.

She was in a breathless state by the time she parked her car in front of the motel. She didn't even know if Devlin was staying at the same one he had stayed at before. If he wasn't, she would have to call all the motels in town and that would take time.

The air was decidedly cooler on her heated face as she got out of the car and went into the motel lobby. Her heart pounding, she approached the desk and asked for Devlin. She was lucky. "Yes," the young man told her, "Mr. Halliday is here. Room thirty-six."

Even the same suite. Perhaps he was more of a creature of habit than she had thought.

"Thank you," she said, trying not to let the way he was eyeing her elegant dress bother her. It was early evening, after all.

Despite all her lectures to herself about aggressive bravery, her knees were shaking by the time they had carried her down the hall to the door where the gold numbers thirty-six rested just at her eye level. She raised her hand to knock, hesitated, clenched her fist tighter, and rapped on the door.

Nothing moved, nothing stirred. She rapped again, harder this time. Still no response. She made an exasperated sound in her throat, and sagged against the doorframe, her enthusiasm and self-confidence draining away. The door swung open.

Devlin stood inside, wearing the silvery robe she had once worn. He had been in the shower, obviously, his hair was damp and the silky robe was clinging to his thighs and chest in places where the moisture caught at the fabric. If she had thought he

175

would be overjoyed to see her, she was mistaken. Cool reserve was the only emotion she could see in the fathomless depths of his eyes. Dear God, was he going to let her stand in the hall forever?

In a husky whisper she asked, "May I come in?"

He stepped back, giving her wordless permission to enter. Her nerves singing with tension, she walked round him and stood in the middle of the room, unsure of what to do next, wishing fervently she were a thousand miles from this room and this man.

"I'm sorry. I've caught you at a bad time."

He shrugged and the action parted the folds of his robe, exposing more of that tanned skin on his chest and the dark hairs that curled there. "No problem."

She had expected something from him, she didn't know what exactly, anger perhaps, or temper, but not this cool indifference. Badly shaken, she said, "May I sit down?"

"Please do." He was so damn polite he made her heart ache. She walked to the round table. The chair was a heavy leather-upholstered one with arms, and of course, she had trouble pulling it out. He didn't help her, he merely watched her struggle with it, until at last she pulled it clear of the table and sank into it. By this time her own temper was simmering. "You're making me sorry I came," she muttered.

He folded his arms and continued to stand watching her as if she were a peculiar specimen swimming around in an aquarium. "Why did you come?"

"I came because I—" She faltered, words failing her. The carefully rehearsed speech, the explanation about how she wanted to come to him with all restraints and barriers gone and the past behind her, even the specter of Jed's stock made into something tangible that would educate their child, all those sane reasonable words dissolved. In their wake was left the overriding need to express her feelings in words. She slanted her chin up-

176

ward, her eyes meeting his. "I came because I love you," she said, "and because I can't live without you."

He didn't move. His brown eyes traveled over her, seeing . . . what? Oh, God, she didn't know what. If he didn't take her in his arms soon she would have to walk out that door, knowing she had given him everything, her company, her pride, her love. Had he ever wanted her love? Had he only wanted her company?

He said, "What about Jed's . . . offer?"

She laughed nervously and opened her purse. "I took it," she said, holding the paper toward him. "I—told him to put the stock in our child's name."

His eyes flared, the pupils darkening, and she knew at once what she had done. "No." She shook her head and another nervous laugh escaped her throat. She stuffed the piece of paper back in her purse, since he obviously wasn't interested in seeing it, and by some miracle her sense of humor reasserted itself. "I'm not sure how I managed to think of it; I'm not expecting a child—at least not yet." Every muscle in her body strained upward, her feminine pride flying like sparks from her eyes. "I thought perhaps we might—work on that . . . unless you've changed your mind. . . ."

"I haven't changed my mind," he said, not moving. "I'm just wondering what made you change yours."

No longer able to sit still, she got up out of the chair, braced herself against the back of it, and said huskily, "You made me change my mind. When you walked out that door, I realized that I—that nothing in my life was worth the loss of you." Still he didn't move, and a numbness crept into her veins, the anesthesia the body provides when the pain is too overwhelming to be borne.

She gripped the chair for a moment and then, somehow, gathered the tiny pieces of confetti that were her nerves and veins and muscles and said, "I've handed you my soul, Devlin, and every part of me that goes with it. I can't do any more." She made a

177

helpless gesture with her hands. "I don't know what else I can say to convince you."

"Yes, I know," he said, and the soft intensity of those words sang through her like a well-placed arrow. "How does it feel, Carolyn? How does it feel to put everything on the line and then not be believed?"

Her face contorted in an agony of pain, the instinctive outcry that followed low and full of distress. "You were teaching me a lesson. . . ." She spun into flight, crossing the room in a run. Just as she passed him, he reached out, caught her, and pulled her to him, his hands claiming her through the thin chiffon. He folded her into his arms—but it was like trying to hold an avenging angel. She struggled against him, pushing at him with her palms, thrusting her hips against his in violent attempts to escape his steely hold.

Her nerves, already pulsing with fury and anguish, jangled with a new warning as hard male thighs pressed against hers, and expert fingers gripped her back, molding her body to his. Her struggling only made her more acutely aware of his masculinity. She forced her body to stillness in his arms and took another avenue of resistance. "Let go. Oh, God, how could you do this to me?"

His hands clamped round her like velvet chains, and within the circle of his arms memories rose in her mind. She remembered his caresses, his touches, his tender, passionate lovemaking. . . . "Because our life together depends on it."

She stared up at him, tears glittering in her eyes.

"Everything hinges on how well I taught you this lesson, Caro—and how well you learned it." His eyes told her that he, too, was feeling the imprint of her body on his. She made a small, wriggling movement that only served to fit her more closely to him. Her whole body registered the hardness of his thighs, the imprint of his hands on her back. He gazed down at her, taking in the flush of her cheeks, the unmistakable darkening of her eyes. "But you always were an apt pupil."

Her body ceased struggling by a will of its own, and instinctively she tilted her head to his lowering one. For another instant he hesitated, until she burned with impatience to feel his lips on hers. Then, at last, he took her mouth in a light, caressing kiss, a kiss that was all the more provocative because it teased, asked, cajoled. When he had her leaning toward him, kissing him back with all the relieved intensity she was feeling, his mouth left hers. He kissed a leisurely path around her face, touching his lips to her eyelids that were closed in sensual pleasure, to her cheeks, to the sensitive lobe of her ear. In one instant that warm mouth changed her body from a quivering mass of fiery pride to a melting receptacle for his touch, his kiss. She fought the drowning feeling with words. "What other lessons do you have to teach me, Mr. Halliday?" she murmured. He pushed the chiffon coverup aside and bent his dark head to explore the creamy exposed skin with that devastating mouth.

"There is an extended course I had in mind," he murmured against her skin, "but it will take years of study."

"Will there be any—tutoring from the instructor after class?"

"I might be able to fit in some special sessions."

"Night school?" The laughter lurked in her voice, and he raised her head and brushed his lips over her mouth. "And day school," he murmured huskily, "and morning school, and any-damn-time-of-the-day-we-feel-like-it school."

He turned her, urging her to walk. Her feet moved, she wasn't sure how. They were disconnected from her brain, yet every nerve in her seemed joined to the man who guided her so tenderly through the doorway into the bedroom part of the suite. One small lamp was on beside the bed. He backed her toward it, and when he would have leaned over her and pressed her down, she came to life and moved quickly, twisting him around, so that the momentum he had meant to carry her down caused him to overbalance and fall first. He reacted with lightning-quick reflexes, twisting away to keep from crushing her. He crashed down on his back, his hold on her arms tightening to take her with him. She landed on his chest, making the air whoosh from his lungs in a muttered grunt of sound.

"For a slender lady," he protested, "you fall like a ton of bricks."

Her legs caught between his, and her toes still touching the floor, she gyrated her hips in a slow, circular motion. "Want me to get up?"

"I'll think about it." His eyes scanned her flushed features, and she smiled down at him, her love radiating from her face. He reached up to touch the smooth surface of her cheek. "I've missed you."

"I've missed you," she said, leaning forward, the provocative tip of her tongue coming out to flick at his lips. He lay still, feigning indifference, but she probed deeper, exploring the underside of his upper lip, and finally the warm darkness of his mouth. As her tongue probed over his, a shudder rocked his body, its intensity pulsing against her own.

"Nice of you to be so conveniently undressed," she whispered, lifting up to pull at the tie of his robe.

"Conveniently undressed?" He lifted a dark, mocking eyebrow. "For what?"

"For this," she murmured, pulling the robe away and exposing the lean maleness of his body to her worshiping eyes. She laid her palms against his chest, feeling boldly wanton as she slid her fingers through the dark chest hair and found the male nipples that were already hard with arousal. She bent her head and explored the tiny buds with her tongue, and under her hips she felt his body's instant reaction to her caressing mouth.

"I think the teacher is going to be learning something from his pupil," he murmured in a low growl.

She let her tongue explore the hollow of his throat, trailed her mouth up to his ear, where she nipped his lobe lightly, then moved down under the firm jaw to his throat and shoulder, alternately giving him tiny little love bites and kisses.

He made a low, throaty sound and rolled, taking her with him, trapping her under his lean frame, the robe tangling underneath her. "I was right, you know."

"Arrogant male," she murmured. He punished her with her own treatment, his teeth and lips exploring the roundness of her now naked shoulder. "What were you right about?"

"The streak of wildness. It's one of the things I love about you."

She was still suddenly, her eyes going to his. "Do you love everything about me, Devlin?"

He knew what she was referring to, and he was sorry that somehow the circumstances of her birth had intruded on their lovemaking. He didn't want her to think about the world outside, not just now. He gave her a roguish grin. "What do you want from me, an out-and-out confession of my total infatuation?"

"I want," she said, struggling to sit halfway up on the bed, "some assurance that my illegitimacy makes no difference to you."

His smile faded. "I've already told you it doesn't. How could it possibly?"

"How will we explain to our children?"

"When they need to know it, we'll tell them the truth," he said matter-of-factly.

"But what about your parents? Devlin, I don't even know if you have parents."

"I do," he said gravely. "My father is dead, but my mother lives in New York City. She'll be delighted with you. She's wanted a daughter-in-law for years."

"She won't compare me to your first wife?"

Devlin said, "She'll be too happy to even think of it." His fingers moved over her shoulders. "If you want to talk about any remaining barriers between us, let's talk about this dress—"

His hands pulled at the stretchy top, and instantly the creamy roundness of her came into view.

He bent to her, his hair brushing her sensitive skin, his mouth finding the circumference of her breast. His moist tongue washed the underside of a curve. Slowly, leisurely, he explored the silken, heated flesh, his hands moving down, taking her dress with them over her hips. Still tantalizing her breasts with little forays that stopped just short of that sensitive center, he divested her of her last remaining tiny garment.

She helped him out of his robe, thinking that this was heaven complete, herself complete. The other part of her, the missing part, was here, in the lithe and well-conditioned male wearing nothing but a look of desire in his eyes as he lay down beside her and gathered her into his arms. He whispered soft words to her, love words. He told her how beautiful she was as he kissed the hollow of her navel, the tiny brown mole at the top of her left thigh. Those warm wonderful hands learned again her secrets, in a way as old as time, yet new and devastatingly different. His mouth moved over her, giving, taking, finding, until she cried out, first in protest, then in delight, her hands going to his shoulders to clutch them in tortured rapture.

He took her to the brink. Clinging on a thread of control, she murmured his name. He understood. Lifting his head, he moved over her, his warm thighs nudging between hers, his hands underneath her to lift and mold her to his masculine contours. At last, when she ached with need, he fitted himself into the softness that waited for him.

It shouldn't have happened, but it did. An incredible starburst of feeling exploded inside her. She clung to him and cried his name, knowing that this was the center of her life, that here was the man who made her whole. She was floating, flying, and he was the orchestrator of her free-fall through space. "I love you," she cried, threading her hands through his hair. He groaned his answer in a hoarse voice, "Love me like this always, Carolyn." He sounded driven, almost desperate. It was her last coherent thought before she was flung into a universe of sensation that burned everything away but her love for Devlin.

"How soon can we be married?" Devlin lay beside her, idly tracing a path from the hollow of her throat to her navel and back again, his warm fingers sending tiny shivers in their wake. *Always ask for more than you want.* "Two weeks?"

He remembered at once. "One," he said huskily.

She smiled and snuggled against him. "All right, one. We'll ask Jed and your mother. . . ." In another moment she was frowning, the fine dark brows drawing together. "Are you sure your mother won't object to my being—"

He interrupted with a mildly exasperated "If you want to worry, worry about something more pressing. Put your agile mind to the logistics of arranging our lives so we can be together."

"But I didn't think that would be a problem."

"I have to be with you," he murmured, his hand cupping her breast, "but I can't justify interrupting your career by taking you away from Leisure Days. The only alternative I have is to offer you a concurrent executive position in my company. That will mean I'll spend a lot of time flying around the country, but—it can't be helped." His mouth sought the circumference of her breast, his tongue stroking just below the rosy, sensitive peak. "Will you accept?"

The joy was almost more than she could absorb. "Oh, Devlin, of course I accept. I'd do anything to be with you."

"Are you sure?" he murmured, favoring her other breast with the same attention that was sending violent tingles to the pit of her stomach.

"Devlin, how could I refuse such a wonderful offer"—she smiled at him, a gleam of mischief in her eyes—"especially when it's negotiated in such an—unusually persuasive way?"

He lifted his head and gazed down at her. "I want you to be very sure it's what you want to do," he said softly.

His concern for her career as well as his love for her as a

woman melted her heart. "It's what I want to do," she said, her breath catching as his head bent and he traced a warm sensual path with his tongue to her navel.

"I'm glad." His husky murmur sent his warm breath fanning the hypersensitive skin of her abdomen. "Because your very first task will be to go to DNR tomorrow morning and begin the necessary paperwork required to build a dock on the river for Leisure Days Houseboats."

She reacted like a cat thrown in water, catapulting upward, pushing against him with her hands and legs. She didn't move him an inch. She tried to brace her arms and keep him away, but her palms merely felt the vibrations of his silent laughter as he leaned over her.

"Devlin! You can't be serious. It'll take forever and be frustrating as hell."

"I know, honey." His eyes glistened with amusement. "But I have full confidence in your ability to get the job done."

"Devlin—"

His smile was roguishly wicked. "As vice-president in charge of LDH, your first priority will be to get that dock built and get it in the water as fast as you can."

She glared at him, her eyes sparkling. "It'll take tons of paperwork and months of time!" Her sense of humor reasserted itself and she grinned up at him and said impishly, "I could make a baby faster."

He moved his hips over and covered her naked body with his own. "That, honey, is your second priority."

"Second?"

"You can work on them both at the same time," he murmured, his mouth covering hers, his hands going on journeys of rediscovery, unearthing new, sensitive places she hadn't known existed, the hollow at the nape of her neck, the indentation at the base of her spine, the inside of her elbow. Huskily he muttered in her ear, "I wonder what you'll finish first."

Her resistance melted. "Well, I certainly know which one I'll enjoy working on the most," she said, laughing, throwing her arms around his neck and pulling him close, giving her mouth to him in joyous abandon.

DELL BOOKS
P.O. BOX 1000, PINEBROOK, N.J. 07058

CHANGE OF HEART $3.50 (11355-5)

B073A

Please send me the above title. I am enclosing $ _____
(please add 75¢ per copy to cover postage and handling). Send check or money
order—no cash or C.O.D.'s. Please allow up to 8 weeks for shipment.

Mr/Mrs/Miss _____

Address _____

City _____ State/Zip _____

At your local bookstore or use this handy coupon for ordering.

"THE MOST ROMANTIC NOVEL SINCE LOVE STORY"
—Good Housekeeping

Change of Heart

SALLY MANDEL

Once in a long while, a story is so bursting with tenderness that its charm is irresistible. That story is Sharlie and Brian's story. *Change of Heart*— a love story for a lifetime.

$3.50

Candlelight Ecstasy Romances™

Candlelight Ecstasy Romances™

$1.95 each

Candlelight
Ecstasy Romances™

Candlelight Ecstasy Romances™

$1.95 each

At your local bookstore or use this handy coupon for ordering:

B073E

DELL BOOKS
P.O. BOX 1000, PINE BROOK, N.J. 07058-1000

Please send me the books I have checked above. I am enclosing $ _____ (please add 75¢ per copy to cover postage and handling). Send check or money order—no cash or C.O.D.'s. Please allow up to 8 weeks for shipment.

Name _____

Address _____

City _____ State Zip _____

CANDLELIGHT Ecstasy Supreme

- [ ] 1 **TEMPESTUOUS EDEN,** Heather Graham 18646-3-37
- [ ] 2 **EMERALD FIRE,** Barbara Andrews 12301-1-10
- [ ] 3 **WARMED BY THE FIRE,** Donna Kimel Vitek 19379-6-12
- [ ] 4 **LOVERS AND PRETENDERS,** Prudence Martin 15013-2-12
- [ ] 5 **TENDERNESS AT TWILIGHT,** Megan Lane 18574-2-17
- [ ] 6 **TIME OF A WINTER LOVE,** Jo Calloway 18915-2-15
- [ ] 7 **WHISPER ON THE WIND,** Nell Kincaid 19519-5-13
- [ ] 8 **HANDLE WITH CARE,** Betty Jackson 13424-2-44
- [ ] 9 **NEVER LOOK BACK,** Donna Kimel Vitek 16279-3-43
- [ ] 10 **NIGHT, SEA, AND STARS,** Heather Graham ...16384-6-29
- [ ] 11 **POLITICS OF PASSION,** Samantha Hughes......16991-7-16
- [ ] 12 **NO STRINGS ATTACHED,** Prudence Martin 16416-8-54

$2.50 each